TIMBERS WORLD..

C000039736

1

AFRICA

Prepared by **W. H. Brown,** FIWSc
In collaboration with TRADA publications panel

Published by
TIMBER RESEARCH AND DEVELOPMENT ASSOCIATION
Hughenden Valley, High Wycombe, Buckinghamshire HP14 4ND, England

AVAILABILITY
Before specifying, it is advisable to check on the commercial
availability of the timbers described in this booklet.

PRINTING HISTORY
Published 1942 as 'Timbers of British West Africa'
Revised 1945 as 'Timbers of West Africa'
Revised 1950
Revised 1968
Reprinted 1972
Reprinted 1975
New edition 1978 as 'Timbers of Africa'

ISBN 0 901348 43 0

© Timber Research and Development Association 1978

Typography by Trevor Tredwell, AMIMPtg
Maps prepared by Tim Wheeler, Henley-on-Thames
Printed by Executive Press Ltd, Burnham, Bucks

CONTENTS

Introduction   Forests of Africa

PART I   HARDWOODS

PART II SOFTWOODS

INTRODUCTION

In 1945 the Timber Development Association, as it was then known, revised a Red Booklet entitled 'Timbers of British West Africa' and republished it as 'Timbers of West Africa'. At that time only a few African timbers were well known to the trade, mainly from the west coast, and the need for information regarding what were then lesser known timbers, was great and for many years the original content and geographical coverage of the booklet was considered adequate. It was revised in 1968 and again in 1972, by the Timber Research and Development Association, and together with its companion booklets, 'Timbers of South East Asia', and 'Timbers of South America', has provided a useful service to trade and industry by detailing the practical characteristics of many commercial timber species from these areas.

Timber as a major raw material is in greater demand and, in consequence, there is a greater need for a wide knowledge of the world's timber resources. With this in mind, the Timber Research and Development Association intend to publish a series of booklets giving a wider and more adequate account of the commercial timbers of the world.

In this, the first of the new series, Africa is considered as a whole, but with a few minor omissions as to geographical forest areas.

In the north of the continent, to a great extent the Atlas mountain regions form part of the south European botanical zone and accordingly, species of poplar, lime and oak, which occur in Morocco, for example, are not included in this booklet but are dealt with more appropriately in the companion 'Timbers of Europe'.

Layout of the booklet

The timbers are placed in two groups, ie hardwoods and softwoods, and are arranged in alphabetical order of their common names; these names are the standardised ones given in BS 881 and 589: 1974: 'Nomenclature of commercial timbers, including sources of supply'.

A guide to the uses of African timbers is given and tables provide information on their resistance to termites and marine borers, and their degree of permeability in regard to preservative treatment.

DURABILITY

Durability, or resistance to decay is important when woods are selected for certain uses where the conditions are favourable for decay to occur. Sapwood is nearly always perishable, but generally more permeable than heartwood, consequently it should not be used in exposed situations without preservative treatment. Heartwood varies in its natural resistance to decay according to the species and the amount of decay inhibiting substances contained in the wood.

The various grades of durability mentioned in the text are those resulting from exposure tests carried out in the United Kingdom and accordingly, are approximate values applicable to areas with similar climate.

The tests refer to all-heartwood stakes of 50mm x 50mm section driven in the ground as stakes. The five durability grades are defined as follows:

Perishable	Less than 5 years when in contact with the ground.
Non-durable	5–10 years when in contact with the ground.
Moderately durable	10–15 years when in contact with the ground.
Durable	15–25 years when in contact with the ground.
Very durable	More than 25 years when in contact with the ground.

FORESTS OF AFRICA

Only about 10 per cent of the total land area of the African continent is covered with forests; tropical hardwoods predominate, comprising about 96 per cent of the forests, with temperate hardwoods accounting for about 3 per cent, and softwoods only about 1 per cent.

North Africa
Forest vegetation has largely disappeared from Algeria and Tunisia, but there is still some forest land in Morocco where the trees have a close affinity with those of Spain and Portugal.

West and East Africa
The great forest areas are the tropical forests which cover the coastal belt of West Africa, from Guinea to Gabon, and which extend into the basin of the Congo. To the east of the Great Rift Valley, Uganda, Kenya, and Tanzania, all have large forest areas, as does also Angola in the south-west, and Mozambique in the south-east.

Two types of forest occur; the mature, or 'high' forests are typical of the tropical or rain forests where rainfall exceeds 1500mm per year without prolonged dry periods. The heaviest rainfall occurs in the coastal areas of the west, where it averages about 4000mm per year. An open, park-like forest occurs in regions where the rainfall amounts to 750mm to 1000mm per year. Large areas of these dry-savannah forests occur in East Africa, Angola and Rhodesia, particularly, but similar fringe-forests occur in West and Central Africa.

Forest reserves, owned by regional governments or local authorities of the various countries are administered under strict control. Nigeria for example has some 2 million hectares of high forest reserves, either under exploitation or leased to timber concessionaires, who hold exclusive felling rights. There is also a large area of roughly 6 million hectares of savannah forest reserves in which usable but scattered quantities of timber trees occur. In addition to the reserves, there are large areas of forest not so strictly controlled, which produce about 50 per cent of Nigeria's total volume of timber.

South Africa

South Africa is poorly endowed with natural forests capable of producing good timber trees, because well over 73 per cent of the surface of the Republic has an annual rainfall of less than 635mm and summer temperatures are high. If the scattered cedar trees on the Cedarberg of Clanwilliam and on the Baviaanskloof Mountains, and the savannah forests of the Transvaal and Natal low-veld are disregarded—because they are not true forests, it is possible to say briefly that indigenous timber forests occur as a non-continuous belt in the region of high rainfall extending east and north-east from Table Mountain to the North-Eastern Transvaal.

The only really extensive wooded areas in South Africa are in the George-Knysna region, where there are more than 48,000 hectares of timber forest on the narrow plateau between the ocean and the Duteniqua and Tsitsikamma Ranges.

Because the indigenous tree species were, especially on account of their slow growth, unsuitable for afforestation, South Africa has imported trees for this purpose, and state-owned plantations have progressively been established, concentrating on the cultivation of *Eucalyptus* species from Australia, and various pines from the Mediterranean, Mexico and the southern USA. South Africa is now more self-sufficient in respect of timber and timber products; the main industries, mining, fruit farming and wine production, absorb much indigenous timber for waggon building, railway sleepers, boxes, crates, etc, while timber from maturing introduced tree species, has improved the range of woods required for consumer goods and for building purposes. Exports of timber and allied products from South Africa consist mainly of flooring timber, rayon and paper pulp, fibre-board, chipboard, plywood and matches.

Consumption of timber in South Africa for all purposes was 5.3 million cubic metres in 1972, and the demand is expected to grow to 23 million cubic metres by the year 2000.

PART I HARDWOODS

ABURA

Mitragyna ciliata Andrew & Pellgr.   Family: Rubiaceae

Other names
subaha (Ghana) ; bahia (French W Africa) ; elilom (Cameroons) ; elelome (Gabon) ; maza, voukou, vuku (Zaire) ; mujiwa, mushiwa.

Distribution
Occurs in West Tropical Africa from Sierra Leone through Liberia and other coastal countries to the Cameroons and Gabon. It is probable that most of the wood exported is *M. ciliata* from the rain forests, since the botanically associated *M. stipulosa* grows outside this zone.

The tree
Abura attains a height of 30m to 40m with a diameter of 1.0m to 1.2m. The tree is free of buttresses, and the bole is straight and cylindrical.

The timber
Pale, reddish-brown to light brown, sapwood wide but not differentiated from heartwood. Grain straight to interlocked, sometimes spiral grain present. Texture fairly fine and very even, sometimes figured like Canadian birch. Rather soft, weight varies from 480 to 640 kg/m^3 dried (average 580 kg/m^3). Fairly resistant to acids.

Drying
Air and kiln dries well and with little degrade. Very stable when dried.

Strength
A timber with medium strength properties, resembling those of common elm.

1

Durability
Not very resistant to decay.

Working qualities
Works well and cleanly with hand and machine tools; takes a good finish; stains, paints, and polishes well. Holds nails and screws, and glues well. One of the best West African timbers for small mouldings. Some logs may have 'spongy heart', and are then difficult to work.

Uses
Interior joinery, fittings, cabinets, mouldings and floors, turnery, plywood and interior doors. Owing to its resistance to acids it is valuable for battery and accumulator boxes. It is a first-class general utility wood.

AFARA

Terminalia superba
Engl. & Diels.

Family: Combretaceae

Other names
The timber has various names according to the part of West Africa from which it comes; the following list gives the most common names with their corresponding countries of origin.

Nigeria: white afara.
Zaire and Angola: limba clair or light limba, limba noir or dark limba, according to the colour of the heartwood.
French West Africa: limbo, chêne limbo, fraké, noyer du Mayombe, akom.
Ghana: ofram.
Liberia: limba, korina.

Some confusion has arisen regarding the difference between white afara and black afara. Actually these are two entirely different species; black afara is *Terminalia ivorensis* and it is usually (and more correctly) known as idigbo. The confusion has been greater because the descriptive adjectives 'white' and

2

'black' were thought to refer to the colour of the wood, since in the case of white afara the heartwood is often grey, streaked with black; black afara (idigbo), paradoxically, is of a uniform pale yellow colour. This anomaly is simply explained; the colours refer to the bark and not to the timber.

Distribution
It is widely distributed in West Africa from Sierra Leone to the Cameroons.

The tree
Afara is a very large tree, from 18m to 45m high. The wide, spreading buttresses may extend up the bole for 2.5m or more, but the bole above is straight and cylindrical with a diameter of about 1.5m. Felling is carried out above the buttress.

The timber
Usually both the heartwood and sapwood are light yellowish-brown in colour, similar to light oak. Occasionally, however, the heartwood contains irregular greyish markings, with streaks which may be almost black (the cause of these markings is not known). Such timber is very attractive in appearance and fetches good prices, being valuable for veneer; off-centre peeling and quarter slicing give the best striping effects. This variation in colour has resulted in the timber from Zaire being divided into two types:—

1 Limba clair (or limba blanc), in which two-thirds or more of the diameter of the log is light in colour.
2 Limba noir (or limba bariolé), in which the dark-coloured heartwood is sufficient to show on the sides of squared logs.

The timber is close-grained and usually straight, but may be wavy in the grain; the latter type providing a good figure. It is of medium hardness and weighs about 560 kg/m^3 when dried (to 15 per cent moisture content).
In large logs the heart may be brittle, and if this is the case, it should be eliminated ('boxed out') in conversion.

Drying
In air drying, there is a tendency for the heart or 'brash' wood to split and shake, but little trouble is experienced with close-

ringed outer wood; fairly thick sticks (25mm) assist in preventing discoloration. Kiln drying is easy, and there is less tendency for defects to develop.

Strength
Complete strength tests have not been carried out, but limited tests indicated that the timber is not very strong, and the dark coloured wood tends to be more brittle than the light, which is fairly resistant to shock loads.

Durability
Afara is not resistant to decay and frequently the heartwood of the larger trees is unsound when felled. The sapwood is liable to blue sapstain. The logs are liable to be attacked by pin-hole borers, which affect both heartwood and sapwood. Powder-post beetles tend to attack the sapwood if care is not taken.

Working qualities
The timber works easily with hand and machine tools; this includes turning. In cases where the grain is uneven there is some tendency to pick up in planing, but this can usually be overcome by using a low cutting angle. Gluing presents no difficulties, and an excellent finish can be obtained. The timber can be stained and polished easily (if a filler is used). Care must be taken in nailing and screwing to avoid splitting.

Uses
The light coloured wood is suitable for face veneers for doors, high quality plywood and furniture, and in appearance is rather like light oak. The more greenish-grey wood is used for core veneer, utility plywood, light construction work such as school equipment, office desks and furniture. The black heart, is very decorative and is suitable for veneer, panelling, furniture, etc. Since grading, especially in Nigeria, is usually based on the degree of pin-worm hole present, the terms 'worm free', 'almost worm free', and 'worm-holes considered' have special significance in terms of end use. A degree of pin-worm hole is therefore not necessarily a defect when the requirement is for painting, or for blockboard cores.

AFRORMOSIA

Pericopsis elata van Meeuwen.   Family: Leguminosae
Syn. *Afrormosia elata* Harms.

Other names
kokrodua (Ghana, Ivory Coast); assamela (Ivory Coast).

Distribution
Afrormosia is found in the Ivory Coast, Ghana and Zaire, and to a small extent in Nigeria.

The tree
A large tree (except in Nigeria), it reaches a height of 45m and a diameter of 1.2m or slightly more.

The timber
Sapwood small, about 12mm wide, slightly lighter in colour than the brownish heartwood. When first cut the heartwood is yellowish-brown, darkening on exposure to a pleasing brownish-yellow, somewhat resembling teak, but with a finer texture, and lacking the oily nature of teak.
The grain is straight to interlocked, and the wood weighs about 710 kg/m^3 when dried.

Drying
Dries rather slowly, with little degrade.

Strength
Afrormosia is superior to teak in most of its mechanical properties and is very similar to home grown beech, except in resistance to compression where it is about 20 per cent stronger.

Durability
Very durable.

Working qualities
The wood works well with only a slight tendency to pick up, but a cutting angle of 20° usually produces a good finish. It can be glued and polished satisfactorily, but tends to split when nailed.

Uses

Afrormosia can be used as an alternative to teak for many purposes where a strong, stable, and durable wood is required. It is used for furniture, high-class joinery, flooring, boatbuilding, shop fitting.

It should not be used in contact with ferrous metals in wet conditions since these may corrode, and the presence of tannins in the wood can cause staining.

AFZELIA

Afzelia spp.   Family: Leguminosae

The trade name afzelia has been proposed for all species of this genus. In practice the West African species are usually grouped together as a single commercial timber. The East African species is usually marketed separately.

The principal species producing West African afzelia are believed to be *A. bipindensis* and *A. pachyloba.*

Other names

A. africana Smith	⎫ doussié (Cameroons and France)
A. bipindensis Harms	⎬ apa, aligna (Nigeria.)
A. pachyloba Harms	⎭
A. quanzensis Welw	chamfuta, mussacossa (Mozambique) mbembakofi, mkora (Tanzania)

Distribution

Afzelia is a transition species found between the savannah forest of dry areas and the dense forests of humid regions. It occurs throughout West Africa, Uganda and parts of Tanzania.

The tree

The West African species attain their greatest size in the moist deciduous forest, with a height of 12m to 18m and a diameter of 1.0m but the bole is relatively short, and rarely straight. In East Africa, it is found mainly in coastal, lowland, and savannah type forests, and is generally smaller, with the bole, above the buttressed base usually about 4.5m high and with a diameter of 1.0m.

The timber
The various species of afzelia are very similar in appearance. The sapwood is pale straw-coloured and sharply defined from the light-brown heartwood; the latter often becomes dark red-brown on exposure. Mottle and other figure is frequently present. The grain is irregular and often interlocked and the texture is coarse but even. It is a hard and moderately heavy wood, weighing about 830 kg/m^3 when dried. Afzelia is an exceptionally stable wood, being comparable to teak in this respect.

Drying
Afzelia species can be kiln dried satisfactorily, but slowly from the green condition. Degrade is not likely to be severe, slight distortion may occur with some fine checking and extension of shakes.

Durability
It is very durable and is reported to be proof against termite and teredo.

Strength
A strong timber, with strength properties comparable with those of oak.

Working properties
Somewhat hard to work, but produces a good finish and may be polished to a very attractive appearance.

Uses
Heavy construction work, especially dock work, bridge building, and flooring. It is a good furniture wood especially when figured; it may be cut into veneer, both for interior decoration and furniture. It can be used for school, office, and garden furniture, staircases, bank counters, laboratory benches, door and window frames, ships rails.

AGBA

Gossweilerodendron balsamiferum   Family : Leguminosae
Harms

Other names
moboron, tola, tola branca, white tola (Angola); ntola, mutsekamambole (Zaire).
This species should not be confused with tchitola, (*Oxystigma, Sindora* and *Oxyphyllum* spp.), sometimes known as tola, tola manfuta, etc.

Distribution
It is found in West Africa, mainly in the western province of Nigeria, but also is found in Angola and Zaire.

The tree
Agba is one of the largest trees of West Africa where it is found in the rain forests. The trunk is cylindrical and free from buttresses; in fact, sometimes the trunk has the appearance of a round log set on end, with no root swelling at the base. The tree is extremely tall and often clear of branches to over 30m, the diameter frequently being 1.5m to 2m.
The bark is thin, greyish, smooth and often showing spiral twisting. If the trunk is wounded or notched, thick gum or oleo-resin exudes which hardens into large lumps. There is considerable variation in respect of gum, some logs being practically free while others contain large quantities.

The timber
There is little difference in colour between the sapwood and the heartwood, the latter is slightly darker but the line of demarcation is somewhat indefinite. The wood varies from yellowish-pink to reddish brown (like a light coloured mahogany). Generally, it strongly resembles mahogany in grain etc, but is less lustrous and paler in colour. The texture is fine and the timber is fairly hard. Particularly when freshly cut the surfaces tend to be gummy. The weight is about 510 kg/m³ when dried.

Drying
The timber can be dried fairly rapidly with very little tendency to warp or split. Some gum exudation is likely to occur, especially in pieces containing the pith, and for this reason, very high temperatures should be avoided.

Strength
Agba is highly resistant to crushing strains; it compares favourably with Honduras mahogany, being about half as tough again and equal in crushing strength, though somewhat less stiff. Brittleheart is often extensive, particularly in large logs. The affected timber is considerably weaker than normal wood, and careful selection is necessary where strength is a requirement.

Durability
The timber is very resistant to decay.

Working qualities
Agba is easy to work with most hand and machine tools; sometimes there is a slight tendency for saws to stick owing to the gumminess of the wood. An excellent finish can be obtained and the wood has good nailing, screwing and gluing properties. It produces good veneer by slicing, but the logs should not be steamed, or the veneer dried under high temperature, because the wood will gum under these conditions.
Generally, agba is similar to Honduras mahogany in working qualities, but usually milder to work. It takes stain and polish well.

Uses
Joinery, interior and shop fittings, turnery, panelling, flooring, sills, furniture, motor bodies and coachwork, toys, veneer and plywood. The large sizes, free from defects, in which it is obtainable, make the wood valuable for many purposes.

AKOSSIKA

Scottellia spp.   Family: Flacourtiaceae

Several species of *Scottellia* occur in west Africa including *S. coriacea* or odoko. Two further species should be mentioned, since their timber is on offer at the present time.
S. chevalieri produces akossika a grande feuilles, and *S. kamerunensis* produces akossika a petites feuilles, the former species being the larger tree, some 30m to 45m tall, and a diameter of 0.4m to 1.0m with a small buttress and a good cylindrical bole, while *S. kamerunensis* attains a height of 30m and a diameter of

0.6m with a long, straight bole which, however, is seldom cylindrical.

The timber
S. chevalieri : Little distinction between sapwood and heartwood which is pale yellow with occasional darker streaks. Grain usually straight, occasionally interlocked; texture fine and even. The wood has an attractive silver-grain figure on quarter-sawn surfaces.
S. kamerunensis : Pale yellow in colour, wood lustrous, grain usually straight, texture medium.
Both species weigh between 580 and 640 kg/m^3 when dry, and both are perishable.

General characteristics
The timbers dry easily, but with a tendency to split and check, and blue-stain occurs, or is liable to occur, during kiln drying. The wood works quite well, takes a good finish, can be glued, and tends to split in nailing. *S. kamerunensis* requires more care in planing and moulding in order to avoid grain pick-up.

Uses
Although *S. chevalieri* appears to be the better wood, both species are used locally for light construction, flooring, furniture, interior joinery, carving, etc. They produce good plywood when staining is avoided.

ALBIZIA, WEST AFRICAN

Albizia spp.   Family: Leguminosae

The numerous species of *Albizia* show considerable variation in the properties of their timbers, and the precise identity of the commercial species is uncertain. The following brief notes summarize the main African species.

Other names
ayinre (Nigeria) ; okuro (Ghana) ; nongo (East Africa).

Distribution
The genus *Albizia* includes at least 30 species in Africa, but

many of these are small trees of the savannah forest. The species from which commercial timber is produced are chiefly trees of the high forest and occur from Sierra Leone through Central Africa to East Africa and Rhodesia.

Main species

A. *adianthifolia* W. F. Wight

A. *ferruginea* Benth.   } West Africa

A. *zygia* Macbride

A. *grandibracteata* Taub.   } East Africa

A. *zygia* Macbride.

Characteristics

A. *ferruginea*. A large tree some 36m in height and 1.0m in diameter, with a clear bole of 9m to 12m. The colour of the heartwood varies from medium brown to dark chocolate-brown, clearly distinct from the yellowish-white sapwood which may be 50mm wide. The grain is decidedly interlocked and often irregular; the texture is coarse. It weighs 640 kg/m^3 dried.

A moderately hard, moderately heavy, very durable timber, with strength properties similar to oak. Fairly easy to work, although irregular interlocked grain may cause tearing in planing. It is said to cause mild irritation of the nose when sawing the dried wood.

A. *zygia*. A tree of medium size, about 27m high and a diameter of 1.0m. It is usually heavily buttressed, but the bole form is good. The heartwood is pale brown, with a pinkish tinge, while the sapwood, which is usually wide (150mm or more), is white, yellowish-white, or grey. The grain may be straight or interlocked, and the texture is coarse. It weighs about 580 kg/m^3 dried; moderately durable, it is susceptible to staining.

A. *adianthifolia*. Common in the secondary forest, the bole is often indented and twisted. The heartwood is light gold or light brown in colour, often with a greenish tinge. The sapwood, like A. *zygia* is very broad and of a creamy-white colour. The wood averages 580 kg/m^3 when dry, possesses a straight or interlocked grain and a moderately coarse texture. It is considered to be moderately durable.

A. *grandibracteata*, together with A. *zygia* is usually marketed in East Africa as red or white nongo, the distinction being one of colour.

Albizia is in abundant supply especially in Nigeria, but lack of demand has so far not resulted in proper commercial production. There would seem to be a case for segregation of the species on a weight basis ie, heavy albizia—640 kg/m^3 or more, and light albizia—under 640 kg/m^3. Uses could include construction, joinery and general carpentry.

ALSTONIA

Alstonia congensis Engl .
& *Alstonia boonei* De Wild.

Family: Apocynaceae

Other names
patternwood, stoolwood (E and W Africa) ; mujua (Uganda) ; ahun, awun, duku (Nigeria) ; tsongutti (Zaire) ; sindru (Ghana) ; emien (Ivory Coast).

Distribution
Abundant throughout the humid forests in the Cameroons ; also found in Sierra Leone, Ivory Coast, Ghana, Nigeria and Zaire. It also grows in Central Africa and Uganda.

The tree
A tall tree, 30m or more in height and up to 1.0m in diameter, with a straight stem.

The timber
Nearly white when freshly cut, the timber darkens slightly on exposure. The sapwood which is not differentiated from the heartwood is very wide and up to 200mm ; soft, and light in weight when dried, the wood weighs about 400 kg/m^3.
The grain is generally straight, and the texture is fine, but the appearance of the wood is often marred by latex canals (slit-like holes about 6mm across) which often occur at regular intervals. The wood also is liable to staining.

Drying
Alstonia dries rapidly and well with practically no distortion.

Strength
Similar to obeche except in shock loading, when it is inferior.

Working qualities

Works easily with all hand and machine tools, but because of the softness of the wood, sharp cutting edges are essential. Can be glued, stained and polished satisfactorily.

Uses

Boxes, crates, rough carpentry for interior work.

ANINGERIA

Aningeria spp.   Family: Sapotaceae

Other names

agnegre (Ivory Coast); landosan (Nigeria); mukali, kali (Angola); mukangu, muna (Kenya); osan (Uganda).
Note: veneer marketed under the misleading names of Tanganyika walnut and noyer de Bassam is believed to be aningeria.

Four species of *Aningeria* occur in tropical Africa, as follows, *A. robusta* is found in West Africa, *A. altissima* occurs in both west and east Africa, *A. adolfi-friederici* is widely distributed throughout East Africa and *A. pseudo-racemosa* also occurs in East Africa, principally in Tanzania.

The tree

The trees are generally tall, commonly 30m to 36m in height, with straight, cylindrical boles some 1.2m to 2.4m in diameter, depending on the species and growth conditions. Bole lengths vary from 27m to 30m above the buttresses, but in *A. altissima* the boles may be shorter owing to the symmetrical winged buttresses which are often tall.

The timber

The wood of the various species is somewhat similar in appearance, and not unlike birch. There is no clear distinction between sapwood and heartwood, except where sap-stain has developed, and the heartwood varies in colour from whitish, to a pale shade of brown, often with a pink tint. The wood is fairly plain in appearance, although quarter-sawn surfaces sometimes show a growth-ring figure, and where wavy grain is present, there is sometimes a slight mottle figure. The wood is lustrous, sometimes with a faint cedar-like scent, and the various species are generally siliceous. The weight when dry varies from 510 kg/m³ to 570 kg/m³. The grain varies from straight to wavy, and the texture from medium to coarse.

Drying
Dries easily and well both in the open and in the kiln apart from the tendency to blue-stain in the early stages of air drying.

Strength
About 20-25 per cent weaker than birch in bending and compression, but comparable in hardness on side grain.

Durability
Perishable.

Working qualities
Reports on the sawing properties of the timber are contradictory, varying from hard due to silica content to easy, but a moderate to severe abrasive action on tools and cutters should be anticipated. In cross-cutting and boring, adequate support is needed to prevent chipping out, and care is needed in planing in order to obtain a smooth finish. The wood takes and holds nails and screws well, and can be glued, stained and polished. The wood can be peeled or sliced for veneer, but for thick veneer for plywood, a softening treatment at 85°C is necessary and encourages a high yield of good veneer which can be dried without distortion and splitting.

Uses
Plywood and veneer, joinery, and general interior utility.

ANTIARIS

Antiaris toxicaria Lesch.   Family: Moraceae
Syn. *A. welwitschii* Engl.

Other names
oro, ogiovu (Nigeria) ; chenchen, kyenkyen (Ghana) ; kirundu (Uganda) ; diolosso (Cameroons) ; ako (Ivory Coast).

Distribution
Widely distributed in the high forest zone of West, Central and East Africa.

The tree
Antiaris may reach a height of 36m to 45m with a diameter of 0.6m to 1.5m. Clear boles up to 21m are common. There are usually no buttresses.

The timber
The timber is white to yellowish-grey, with little difference between heartwood and sapwood; soft, light in weight, averaging about 430 kg/m^3 when dried, and of a fibrous nature. Not very durable nor strong. The timber should be converted and dried as rapidly as possible to prevent staining.

Working qualities
A timber which is easy to saw and work, but liable to tear and pick up on quartered surfaces unless the cutting angle is reduced to 20°. It has good nailing, staining and gluing characteristics.

Uses
It is used for light construction, and as quarter-sliced veneer for furniture. It is not suitable for all-veneer plywood because it is too coarse and too soft.

AVODIRÉ

Turraeanthus africanus Pell   Family: Meliaceae
and *T. vignei* Hutch. and J. M. Dalz.

Other names
apeya, appayia, wansenwa (Ghana); apaya (Nigeria); engan (Cameroons); lusamba, esu, songo (Zaire).

Distribution
These species appear relatively restricted to a coastal belt stretching from Ghana westwards as far as the Bandama River on the Ivory Coast. It is a gregarious species and has also been recorded in Angola.

The tree
A medium-sized tree, from 18m to 30m high with a diameter of about 0.6m. The habit of growth is not good, the trunk often being crooked and irregular.

The timber
There is generally no clear distinction between heartwood and sapwood; the wood is pale yellow with a natural lustre, and darkens to pleasing golden-yellow colour. The grain is sometimes straight but often wavy or irregularly interlocked, producing a beautiful mottled figure when quarter sawn. The appearance of the figured wood suggests East Indian satinwood except it has a more open texture. The weight is about 560 kg/m³ when dried, ie, about the same as African mahogany.

Drying
Avodiré can be dried fairly rapidly, but has some tendency to distort, and existing shakes to extend.

Strength
It is a strong, tough and elastic timber in proportion to its weight.

Durability
Non-durable.

Working qualities
It works fairly easily by both hand and machine tools. In planing it tends to pick up owing to the interlocked grain, and a cutting angle of 20° or less is desirable for a smooth finish. The timber has fairly good nailing, screwing, and gluing properties, takes stain well, and gives good results with the usual finishing treatments.

Uses
Figured material is satisfactory for sliced veneer, high-grade cabinet work and panelling. Plain stock is useful for plywood manufacture, but selection of suitable logs is not always easy.

AYAN

Distemonanthus benthamianus Baill.   Family : Leguminosae

Other Names
anyaran, anyanran, anyan (Nigeria) ; barré (Ivory Coast) ; eyen (Cameroons) ; oguéminia (Gabon) ; movingui (Benin).

Distribution
Ayan is widely distributed in West Africa from the Ivory Coast to Gabon and Zaire.

The tree
This is a slender tree attaining a height of more than 30m but seldom more than 0.75m diameter. The bole is straight, cylindrical and free from buttresses.

The timber
The pale yellow sapwood is narrow and not clearly defined ; the heartwood is pale to bright yellow or yellow-brown. It is fine textured, the grain is often interlocked, sometimes wavy, and the wood has a very lustrous surface. Moderately hard and heavy it weighs about 690kg/m^3 when dried.

Drying
Dries fairly well with little tendency to split and warp.

Durability
Moderately durable.

Strength
Good strength properties, especially in compression along the grain and in bending.

Working qualities
Works well with hand and machine tools ; there is a tendency to pick up when planing quarter-sawn stock owing to inter-locked grain. It takes nails and screws fairly well, finishes excellently, and takes a high polish if sufficient filler is used.

Uses
Furniture, cabinet work, ships fittings, flooring, interior joinery. Owing to the presence of a yellow extractive, which in moist conditions can produce a yellow dye, the wood is not suitable for use as clothes airers, laundry equipment.

17

BANGA WANGA

Amblygonocarpus andongensis   Family : Leguminosae
Exell & Torre

Other names
None.

Distribution
The natural distribution of *Amblygonocarpus* is restricted to the savannah area of Uganda and adjacent territories, extending southwards to Mozambique.

The tree
The tree is small to medium, occasionally reaching 20m in height, with a diameter of about 0.5m.

The timber
The narrow, greyish-white sapwood is clearly defined from the heartwood which is warm brown or brownish-red in colour, with a subdued 'partridge wing' figure on tangential surfaces due to soft tissue which surrounds the pores and links several together.
The wood is hard and heavy, weighing about $1040kg/m^3$ when dried. The grain is rather irregular and sometimes interlocked, but the texture is fine.

Drying
Dries slowly owing to its hardness, and requires extreme care if checking and distortion are to be avoided.

Strength
A heavy, hard, and strong timber, with a high resistance to impact and abrasion.

Durability
Probably very durable.

Working qualities
When dry, it is reputed to work reasonably well, but requires a reduced cutting angle in planing and moulding. There is a tendency to 'ride' on cutters.

Uses
At present, it is best known for heavy duty flooring, but is used for sleepers in East Africa.

BERLINIA

Berlinia spp.,
including *B. bracteosa* Benth.,
B. confusa Hoyle.,
and *B. grandiflora* Hutch. & Dalz.

Family : Leguminosae

Other names
ebiara (Liberia and Gabon) ; ekpogoi (Nigeria) ; abem (Cameroons).

Distribution
The various species of *Berlinia* grow throughout West Africa in various types of forests. The most important timber species occur in the high forest belt of Sierra Leone, Liberia, the Ivory Coast, Ghana, Nigeria and the Cameroons.

The tree
The trees are from 24m to 42m high, and may be up to 1.2m in diameter, with an average of 0.75m at maturity. The trunk is usually without buttresses, but it may be fluted at the base. The bole is reasonably straight, clear and cylindrical.

The timber
The heartwood varies from light red to dark red-brown, with dark purple or brown irregular streaks. The sapwood is pink when freshly cut, but turns whitish or greyish on exposure. Traumatic vertical gum ducts are frequently present, appearing on the cross section in arcs of varying length. The texture of the wood is coarse, and the grain is usually interlocked and sometimes very irregular. Brittleheart may occur in large logs.
The timber is moderately hard and moderately heavy ; the weight is variable but averages 720 kg/m³ when dried.

Drying
Berlinia dries slowly and well and, except for the occasional piece, without distortion. Discoloration from mould growths which tend to develop during kiln drying is a frequent problem.

Strength
Its strength properties compare favourably with English oak.

Durability
Moderately durable.

Working qualities
Since the sapwood band in berlinia is often very wide (100mm to 150mm is common) the amount of sapwood present in the parcel will have a bearing on the working qualities. Sapwood that has relatively straight grain and the less dense heartwood can be worked fairly easily with both hand and machine tools and have a moderate blunting effect on their cutting edges. The tearing that occurs in planing and moulding can be reduced by reducing the cutting angle to 20° unless the wood has wavy grain, when a smooth finish is not possible. When the denser heartwood is cut there is a tendency for ripsaws to vibrate in the cut. Most other operations are satisfactory. Sapwood with highly irregular grain is difficult to stain and polish, but other material stains well. It glues satisfactorily and nails fairly well.

Uses
Carpentry and general cabinet-making. The timber is suitable for the same uses as oak, except for bending. It is also used in vehicle bodies.

AFRICAN BLACKWOOD

Dalbergia melanoxylon   Family : Leguminosae
Guill. and Perr.

Other names
mpingo (Tanzania).
Although this timber is sometimes given the name 'African ebony', it is misleading as the true ebonies have the generic name *Diospyros*; it would therefore be more correct to call it a rosewood since it is a species of *Dalbergia*. The standard name is African blackwood.

The tree
This is a small tree growing to about 9m high, with a clear bole

20

rarely over 2.5m high and a diameter of about 200mm rarely exceeding 300mm. The tree is occasionally multi-stemmed.

The timber
The sapwood is narrow, white in colour, and clearly defined from the dark heartwood, which is dark brown with predominant black streaks which give an almost black appearance to the wood. It is straight grained and extremely fine textured, hard and more dense than rosewoods generally, weighing about 1200 kg/m^3 when dried.

Drying
It is generally partially dried in log or billet form and then converted and stacked under cover to complete the drying. The timber dries extremely slowly and heart shakes are very common. In general the wood needs to be carefully handled to minimize checking.

Durability
Very durable.

Working qualities
In spite of its hardness it works quite easily, and takes an excellent finish. It is however, moderately hard to saw, and requires drilling for nails and screws.

Uses
Ornamental turnery, chessmen, carved figures, walking sticks, inlay work, brushbacks, knife handles, and pulley blocks. Its oiliness and resistance to climatic changes commend it for woodwind instruments in preference to ebony, and it is used in the manufacture of bagpipes, clarinets, piccolos and flutes.

BOXWOOD

Buxus macowani Oliv.   Family: Buxaceae
and *Gonioma kamassi* E. May.   Family: Apocynaceae

The trade name boxwood, originally the English equivalent of *Buxus sempervirens*, has been extended to cover a number of botanically unrelated species with wood resembling true boxwood in general character, eg *Gonioma kamassi, Gossypiospermum praecox* and *Phyllostylon brasiliense.*

Other names
East London boxwood, Cape box (S Africa), *Buxus macowani.* Knysna boxwood, kamassi boxwood, (S Africa) *Gonioma kamassi.*

Distribution
East London boxwood occurs in a strip of forest along the south-east coast of Cape Province, South Africa, while Knysna boxwood occurs in the coastal forests on the south coast of Cape Province.

The tree
East London boxwood is a small tree with a clean bole of about 4.5m to 6m and a diameter of about 150mm at breast height when mature.
Knysna boxwood is a slightly larger tree attaining a height of 6m and a diameter of 300mm.

The timber
The wood of both species is very similar to true boxwood (*Buxus sempervirens*) and while *G. kamassi* weighs about 880 kg/m³ *B. macowani* weighs about 960 kg/m³ when dried.

Drying
The main defect encountered in drying is the development of very fine surface checks, which however, tend to penetrate deeply into the wood, and may open as drying proceeds. Drying is best carried out under cover; small logs being left in the round, and larger ones either cut in halves, or converted to dimension stock. The timber should be allowed to dry very slowly; reports from South Africa suggest four to five months in which to dry 25mm stock in the open air.

Strength properties
No strength data are available, but are probably similar to European boxwood.

Durability
Probably durable.

Working qualities
Fairly hard to work, especially with hand tools, but dulling effect is only moderate. Can be machined to a fine finish, but a reduction of cutting angle to 20° with an increased loading on pressure bars and shoes will minimize the tendency for the wood to 'ride' on the cutters during planing and moulding. Can be turned well; should be pre-bored for nailing and screwing; glues, stains, and polishes well.

Uses
Generally the same as for European boxwood; turnery, engraver's work, small rollers and shuttles for the textile industry.

BUBINGA

Guibourtia spp.   Family: Leguminosae
principally *G. demeusei* J. Léon,
but including *G. pellegriniana* J. Léon,
and *G. tessmannii* J. Léon

Other names
kévazingo (Gabon); essingang (Cameroons).

Distribution
Mostly found in the Cameroons and Gabon.

The tree
The trees attain a height of 24m to 30m with a diameter of 1.0m or more.

The timber
The heartwood is light red-brown attractively veined with pink or red stripes; the sapwood is lighter in colour. The wood is hard and heavy, weighing from 800 to 960 kg/m³ when dried. It has a fine texture.

Uses
Almost exclusively used for decorative veneer; when sliced it is

23

called bubinga, and when rotary cut (which gives a somewhat different figure) it is called kévazingo.

'EAST AFRICAN CAMPHORWOOD'

Ocotea usambarensis Engl.   Family: Lauraceae

Other names
camphor, muzaiti, muura, munganga, mutunguru.

Distribution
Kenya and Tanzania.
Although the timber has a distinct scent of camphor, it should not be confused with Borneo or Sabah camphorwood (*Dryobalanops* spp), or true camphorwood (*Cinnamomium camphora*).

The tree
The largest tree of Kenya, attaining a height of 36m and a diameter of 1.5m to 2.0m and sometimes as great as 3.0m. It is a tree of the mountain and rain forests, occurring on the southern and eastern slopes of Mount Kenya and in the Aberdare Range. In Tanzania it is found on Mount Kilimanjaro, Usambara and Upare.

The timber
The timber, when fresh, is yellowish with a greenish or brownish tinge, darkening to deep brown on exposure. The sapwood is paler, but not always clearly defined. It generally lacks figure, except when quarter cut when it has a pronounced stripe owing to interlocking grain. Texture moderately fine; moderately hard, and moderately heavy, weighing about 610 kg/m^3 when dried. The timber has a camphor like odour when fresh, but this disappears in due course.

Drying
Needs care in air drying as it is liable to warp and twist if this process is too rapid. Kiln drying can be carried out slowly, and with little degrade, but there may be some difficulty in removing the moisture from the centre of thick stock, especially when quarter sawn.

Strength
For its weight, East African camphorwood has extremely good strength properties being superior to American mahogany in most categories.

Durability
Very durable. Reported to be termite resistant.

Working qualities
The timber is easy to work and saw, but needs care in planing quarter-sawn surfaces to prevent the interlocked grain picking-up; a cutting angle not greater than 20° should be used.
The timber can be successfully peeled; it takes nails and screws well, and glues satisfactorily.

Uses
Furniture, panelling, interior and exterior joinery, flooring, light constructional purposes.

CANARIUM, AFRICAN

Canarium schweinfurthii Engle.   Family: Burseraceae

Other names
papo, elemi (Nigeria); abeul (Gabon); abel (Cameroons); mupafu, mbidinkala, mwafu (Uganda).

Distribution
It has a wide distribution stretching from Sierra Leone to Angola and Uganda.

The tree
Canarium attains a large size, sometimes exceeding 30m in height, and 1.2m in diameter above the thickened base. The average length of the clear bole is often between 14m and 15m but may reach 23m in good specimens.

The timber
Light brown or pinkish brown, resembling gaboon (okoumé) in general appearance. The surface is lustrous and the wood is distinctly scented when freshly sawn. The texture is somewhat

coarse and may be woolly; the grain is often spiral. Large logs are liable to contain brittleheart. It weighs on average 530 kg/m³ when dry, which is slightly heavier than gaboon.

Drying
Not unduly difficult to dry although some distortion and even collapse may occur.

Durability
Non-durable.

Strength
Strength properties are similar to agba, especially in regard to stiffness, resistance to compression and shear strength, but it is slightly weaker in bending and shock resistance.

Working qualities
Canarium is a difficult timber to saw; owing to the presence of silica in the wood it blunts saw teeth extremely rapidly.
Planing and moulding is comparatively easy, but sharp cutting edges must be maintained, and a reduced cutting angle of 20° normally provides clean smooth surfaces.

Uses
Canarium is a utility wood for interior joinery and carpentry. It produces good veneer but usually of core quality suitable for plywood.

CEIBA

Ceiba pentandra Gaertn.   Family: Bombacaceae.

Other names
silk cotton tree, okhar (Nigeria); kapokier, fuma (Zaire), fromager (France).

Distribution
Widely distributed in the Eastern hemisphere tropics, it occurs particularly in Nigeria, where it springs up readily in clearings.

The tree
Ceiba grows to a height of 30m to 36m and diameters of 1.2m to 2.0m are common. The trunk is heavily buttressed.

The timber
The wood is whitish with yellowish streaks, or greyish, often with a pinkish tinge. It is often cross-grained and the texture is coarse. Soft, and light in weight, it weighs on average 350 kg/m^3 when dried. It is a dull looking wood, very absorbent, and prone to discoloration unless rapidly extracted, converted and dried.

Drying
Dries well with little degrade such as distortion, splitting and checking.

Durability
Non-durable.

Working qualities
Easily worked, but rather difficult to obtain a smooth finish.

Uses
Sound insulation eg cabin panelling, core stock, and simple carpentry and joinery.

Note: A closely related genus produces West African bombax. This is principally the product of *Bombax buonopozense* P. Beauv. In its general characteristics, colour, and weight, it is very similar to ceiba. Two other species ie *B. breviscuspe* Sprague, known as kondrotti and *B. chevalieri* Pellegr., known as alone have slightly heavier timber, are medium brown in colour and are occasionally shipped. The uses for bombax are the same as for ceiba.

CELTIS, AFRICAN

Celtis spp.   Family: Ulmaceae
principally *C. adolphi-friederici* Engl.,
C. milbraedii Engl.,
C. zenkeri Engl.
syn *C. soyauxii* Engl.

Other names
esa (Ghana) ; ita, ohia, ba (Nigeria) ; shiunza, chia, mudengwa, kiambo (Uganda) ; kerrua, chepkelelet (Tanzania).

Distribution
Celtis is very common in parts of Nigeria and Ghana, and extends from West Africa through Central Africa to Uganda, Tanzania, and part of Kenya.

The tree
An evergreen tree with a straight, fairly heavily buttressed bole. Height 30m and diameter of 1.0m or occasionally more.

The timber
The timber is whitish or greyish in colour turning yellowish or straw coloured on exposure. The grain is irregular, but is sometimes straight, and the texture is fairly fine. The weight averages 800 kg/m^3 in the dry condition.

Drying
Needs care in drying, as it is apt to warp and split.

Strength
For its weight, the strength properties of celtis are, on the whole, rather above the average. In many of its properties it compares favourably with ash.

Durability
Non-durable, and is rapidly attacked by staining fungi in adverse circumstances.

Working qualities
Works well with moderate ease in machine operations, but is slightly hard to work by hand. Straight grained material finishes cleanly in general but there is some tendency to tear out in planing when interlocked grain is present. A cutting angle of 15° is recommended. The timber is inclined to split in nailing, but takes glue, stain and polish well.

Uses
Celtis has been used successfully as a substitute for ash. It is a general utility timber suitable for interior joinery and carpentry. It is a very good flooring material, having a high resistance to wear; there is little surface breakdown, the surfaces wearing smooth, and could be a substitute for maple flooring.

CORDIA

Cordia spp.   Family : Boraginaceae
including *C. abyssinica* R.Br.,
C. millenii Bak.,
and *C. platythyrsa* Bak.

Other names
mukumari, mugona, mringaringa, mungoma (Kenya and Tanzania) ; omo (Nigeria).

Distribution
The African species of *Cordia* occur as a deciduous tree of semi-tropical rain forests in Kenya and Tanzania, and to a lesser extent in West Africa, generally in Nigeria.

The tree
A medium-sized tree averaging 10m high and 0.6m diameter. The bole is generally irregularly shaped.

The timber
The wood is variable in colour, ranging from rich golden-brown to fawn with dark streaks, usually darkening on exposure to a light reddish brown not unlike the associated freijo (*C. goeldiana*) which grows in Brazil. The sapwood is cream coloured. The medium sized rays in cordia promote a mottle figure on quarter-sawn surfaces. A medium-textured wood, generally fairly straight-grained, but occasionally interlocked. Light and moderately soft, it weighs about 480 kg/m^3 when dried.

Drying
Dries easily and well without undue splitting and warping.

Durability
Moderately durable.

Working qualities
The timber is easy to work but sharp tools are needed to prevent the surface from becoming woolly. Nails well, and can be polished effectively if care is taken.

Uses
Furniture, cabinets and library fittings. In Africa it is often used for making traditional drums because of its resonant quality, and for generations has been a canoe making wood in Nigeria. Could also be considered useful for general joinery purposes.

DACRYODES SPECIES

Family : Burseraceae

The following species occur in West Africa :
Dacryodes buettneri; known as ozigo (Gabon)
D. edulis; known as ollem
D. igaganga; known as igaganga (Gabon)
D. klaineana; known as adjouaba
D. le-testui; known as mouvendo
D. normandii; known as ossabel (Gabon)
D. pubescens syn *D. heterotrichia*; known as safoukala (Congo)

The tree
The trees vary in height according to species, from 24m to 36m with diameters ranging from 0.3m to 1.5m.
The boles are generally straight and cylindrical, with the odd specimen, particularly in *D. klaineana*, being irregular. There are generally no buttresses, but some boles may be fluted.
The timber
Dacryodes is botanically associated with gaboon (*Aucoumea klaineana*), and there is some similarity in the general appearance of the wood of all the species.

Ozigo: sapwood not clearly demarcated from the heartwood which is grey-buff in colour. The grain may be interlocked or crossed, or straight, and the texture is rather coarse. The wood has a slight lustre and a ribbon figure on quarter-sawn surfaces. Weight about 650 kg/m³ when dry.

Ollem: similar to ozigo in appearance and colour, but with a medium texture, and with some included resin. Weight about 650 kg/m³ when dry.

Igaganga: sapwood 25–37mm wide, lighter in colour than the heartwood which is a pinkish-buff colour. The grain is usually interlocked, seldom straight, and the texture varies from medium to fine. The wood sometimes produces a decorative figure, but it contains silica and gum ducts. Weight about 650 kg/m³ when dry.

Adjouaba: sapwood paler than the heartwood which is a grey or pink colour. The grain is straight to interlocked, and the texture fine. The wood contains resin. Weight 810 kg/m³ when dry.

Mouvendo: sapwood barely distinguishable from the pink-buff or grey-buff heartwood. Grain wavy or straight, texture medium. Weight about 650 kg/m³ when dry.

Ossabel: sapwood not clearly demarcated from the heartwood which is a pink-buff colour with an occasional grey tinge. The grain is often interlocked, and the texture medium to coarse. Weight about 650 kg/m³ when dry.

Safoukala: sapwood very wide, often extending over half the diameter of the log. The general colour may be pale pink, yellow, or grey with the heartwood a little darker. The grain may be straight or interlocked, and the wood often shows attractive ribbon, or small stripe figure. The texture is moderately fine, and the wood weighs about 750 kg/m³ when dry.

Drying
All species dry quite well, but care is needed in air drying to avoid surface checking.

Strength
Similar to gaboon, but more fissile.

Durability
Non-durable.

Working qualities
All species work and machine reasonably well, although some dulling of cutting edges can be expected due to the silica content. There is a tendency for the grain to pick up in planing and moulding, and a reduction of cutting angle to 15–20° is usually essential, but the wood sands to a good finish. All

species peel well for veneer, and plywood manufactured in Ghana from adjouaba has been reported to compare favourably with Canadian yellow birch. The timber has good nailing and screwing properties, and can be glued, stained and polished satisfactorily.

Uses
Interior joinery, flooring, plywood, boxes and crates.

DAHOMA

Piptadeniastrum africanum   Family : Leguminosae
(Hook f.) Brenan.
Syn. *Piptadenia africana* Hook, f.

Other Names
ekhimi, agboin (Nigeria); dabéma (Ivory Coast); toum (Gabon); atui, tom, bokungu (Cameroons); banzu, musese, singa (Zaire); mpewere, mapewere (Uganda); mkufi (Tanzania).

Distribution
Dahoma is a common species in the rain forests of West, Central, and parts of East Africa, but is more prevalent, and attains its best development in the mixed deciduous forest.

The tree
Dahoma is a large tree usually 36m or more high, but the large, spreading, plank buttresses reduce the usable bole to something like 10m to 15m with a diameter of 1.0m or slightly more. The bole is usually straight and cylindrical.

The timber
Sapwood is whitish to greyish-red, sharply defined from the heartwood which is light to golden-brown, very similar in appearance to iroko. A ribbon grain produces zones of light and dark colour. When freshly cut there is an unpleasant smell resembling ammonia and the sawdust is sometimes irritating to the eyes.
The texture is coarse and woolly, but uniform. It weighs from 560 to 710 kg/m^3 when dried.

Drying
Rather difficult to dry, but variable in this respect. Dries slowly, and there is a tendency to distort, and a liability to collapse in some thick material.

Strength
The strength values are good, resembling those of iroko, but because of interlocking grain it is not suitable for use in small sections where strength in bending is a prime requirement.

Durability
Moderately durable; reported to be resistant to termites.

Working qualities
Works fairly well but with appreciable dulling effect on tools. There is a tendency to pick up in planing, and a cutting angle of 10° is recommended. Takes a good finish and may be screwed and nailed, with only a slight tendency to split when nailed near the edges.

Uses
Domestic flooring, vehicle bodies and floors, structural work and marine uses.

DANTA

Nesogordonia papaverifera Capuron, Family: Tiliaceae
Syn. *Cistanthera papaverifera* A. Chev.

Other names
otutu (Nigeria); kotibé (Ivory Coast); olborbora (Gabon); ovoué (Cameroons); tsanya (Zaire).

Distribution
Danta grows in the mixed deciduous forests in southern Nigeria, the Ivory Coast and Ghana.

The tree
A fairly large tree some 27m to 30m high with a long, cylindrical bole, about 15m high, above the sharp buttress, and with a diameter of about 0.75m.

The timber
The sapwood is light brown with a pinkish tinge and is sharply defined from the heartwood, which is reddish-brown and has a lustrous surface; it has a fine texture, and the grain is typically interlocked and this produces a ribbon figure, the striped appearance on quarter-sawn material resembling sapele. It is hard and fairly heavy, being about 750 kg/m^3 when dried. Planed surfaces have a somewhat greasy feel.

Drying
Dries fairly well with some tendency to warp. Care must be taken to avoid over-rapid drying or there may be a danger of casehardening with 'ribbing' of the surface.

Strength
It is a very strong and elastic timber and some of its mechanical properties are similar to those of European ash. It is however, significantly weaker than ash in its resistance to impact loads and cannot be recommended in place of ash for the most exacting purposes.

Durability
Moderately durable.

Working qualities
Danta works well with most tools, but has a tendency to pick up on quarter-sawn material. It turns excellently and takes a good finish and polishes well.

Uses
Lorry bodies, coach and wagon work, general construction and for purposes where a strong, durable wood is required. It wears smoothly and has a good resistance to abrasion, and is therefore suitable for flooring. It is used for telegraph cross-arms and railway sleepers. In Nigeria it ranks second to celtis in its uses for tool handles, eg files, screwdrivers, etc, and is considered to be superior to mansonia and sycamore as an etching timber in graphic art.

DIFOU

Morus mesozygia Stapf.   Family : Moraceae

Distribution
Tropical Africa, particularly the Ivory Coast.

The tree
Grows to a height of 27m to 36m and a diameter of 0.6m to 0.9m.

The tree has wide spreading root ridges and produces a straight cylindrical bole some 18m in length.

The timber
The sapwood, which is wide in young trees, is pale grey or white in colour, and the heartwood is yellow when freshly cut, darkening with age to coffee brown. It often shows a mottle figure. The grain is shallowly interlocked, and the texture is fine. The wood is often confused with the related iroko, which it resembles in appearance, but difou is a slightly heavier wood, and the texture is finer than that of iroko which also has rather larger pores. Difou weighs about 760 kg/m³ when dry.

Drying
Dries quite well and rapidly, without undue distortion.

Strength
The strength properties are superior to those of iroko, and more nearly approximate those of okan.

Durability
Moderately durable.

Working qualities
Although hard and heavy, difou saws quite satisfactorily, although cutting edges generally tend to dull fairly rapidly. In planing and moulding a reduction of cutting angle to 15° is essential to avoid grain tearing, especially on quarter-sawn surfaces. The wood glues and polishes satisfactorily, and takes and holds nails and screws well. It produces good veneer.

Uses
Heavy construction, flooring, vehicle bodies, furniture, sporting goods, agricultural implements, veneer and plywood, joinery and turnery.

EBONY, AFRICAN

Diospyrus spp.   Family : Ebenaceae
including *D. crassiflora* Hiern.,
and *D. piscatoria* Gurke.

Other names
Cameroons, Gabon, Kribi, Madagascar, Nigerian ebony, according to origin.

Distribution
Limited range in southern Nigeria, Ghana, Cameroons and Zaire.

The tree
A small to medium-sized tree attaining a height of about 18m and a diameter of about 0.6m.

The timber
One of the best jet-black varieties is believed to be *D. crassiflora* It is a very heavy timber weighing 1030 kg/m^3 when dried. Other species produce handsome black and brown striped varieties.

Drying
In general African ebony air dries quite readily, but there is a tendency for surface checks to develop. In small sizes, the timber kiln dries fairly quickly and well, with little tendency to split or distort.

Durability
Probably very durable.

Working qualities
The black heartwood is inclined to be brittle and is rather hard to work, and has a considerable dulling effect on cutters which should have their cutting angle reduced to 20° to avoid picking up when curly grain is present. It takes a fine polish.

Uses
Turnery, inlaid work, fancy articles, brush backs.

EKABA

Tetraberlinia bifoliolata   Family : Leguminosae

Other name
ekop ribi.

Distribution
Found in mixed forests, often in small clusters, particularly in the Cameroons and Gabon.

The tree
A tall tree, it reaches a height of 45–50m and a diameter varying from 0.9m to 2.0m.
The bole is generally straight, clear and cylindrical, and the base is sometimes swollen or fluted.

The timber
The sapwood varies in width from 25mm to 125mm some logs having wide sapwood and brittle heart. There is not much difference by colour between sapwood and heartwood, the wood generally being a pale buff when first cut, turning rapidly to pink, with darker streaks. There is often a greyish tinge to the wood, and hard black kino is often present. The grain is usually interlocked or irregular, and the texture is medium to rather coarse. The wood weighs 720 kg/m³ when dry. Wet wood tends to stain when in contact with iron.

Drying
The timber dries rather slowly but well, with only isolated instances of moderate distortion.

Strength
No data are available.

Durability
Moderately durable.

Working qualities
Works and machines with moderate ease, but there is a tendency for grain tearing to occur in planing and moulding, and a reduction of cutting angle to 20° is necessary in order to obtain

a clean finish. The wood takes stains and polish well, and gluing is satisfactory, although there may be tendency for the glue to show on the wood as dark blotches.

Uses
Flooring, veneer, furniture, cabinets, joinery and turnery.

EKEBERGIA

Ekebergia rueppeliana   Family : Meliaceae
Fresen. ex A. Rich.

Other names
monko, mfuari, mbo, teldet, mukongu, mununga.

Distribution
Found in Tanzania, Uganda, Kenya and southern Rhodesia, commonly in the rain forests.

The tree
A large tree up to 30m high, with a clear bole of 10m and a diameter of 1.0m. The trunk is often fluted and crooked.

The timber
The wood is generally a light pinkish-brown with irregular darker lines. The grain is straight, and the texture is medium to coarse. It weighs about 545 kg/m^3 when dried.

Drying
It is reported to dry fairly well, without undue warping and splitting. It is liable to be attacked by staining fungi if not converted and dried rapidly.

Strength
No information available.

Durability
Non-durable.

Working qualities
The timber is easy to work, nails well, and is reported to take a good finish.

Uses
Interior joinery and furniture.

EKKI

Lophira alata Banks ex Gaertn.   Family: Ochnaceae

Other names
kaku (Ghana); azobé (Ivory Coast); bongossi (Cameroons); akoura (Gabon); eba (Nigeria); hendui (Sierra Leone).

Distribution
Grows in West Africa from Sierra Leone to Nigeria and the Cameroons. It is a tree of the heavy rain forests and swamps.

The tree
Ekki is a large tree, attaining a height of 45 to 50m and a diameter of 1.5m.

The timber
The sapwood is pale pink and sharply defined from the heartwood, which is red-brown to dark brown with a somewhat speckled appearance due to white deposits in the pores. The grain is usually interlocked and the texture is coarse. The wood is extremely hard and heavy, weighing 960 to 1120 kg/m^3 when dried.

Drying
Very difficult to dry and generally shakes badly; serious degrade is likely, especially surface checking and end splitting. Needs to be piled with special care.

Durability
Very resistant to decay; one of the most durable woods yet known in West Africa.

Working qualities
Very difficult to work with hand tools, but can be worked by machines with less trouble. Must be pre-bored for nailing.

Uses
Too hard for some purposes, but is suitable for heavy construc-

tion especially wharves, bridge building and decking, sleepers, flooring—especially heavy duty flooring. It is ideal for all forms of marine work for piling, sea defences, groynes and jetties, and any use where high strength and durability is a prime requirement.

EKOUNE

Coelocaryon klainei　　　　　　　　Family : Myrtaceae
Syn *C. preussii*

Distribution
West Africa principally in Gabon and Congo.

The tree
Grows to a height of 30m and a diameter of 0.3m to 0.9m with a clean, straight, and cylindrical bole, usually unbuttressed, of some 12–18m in length.

The timber
There is generally little difference in colour between sapwood and heartwood ; the sapwood is very wide, white or pale pinkish-yellow in colour, darkening on exposure. The heartwood is pale brown, occasionally reddish-yellow, with dark markings. The wood is lustrous, with a straight grain, and with a medium to fine texture. It varies in weight between 650 kg/m^3 to 720 kg/m^3 when dry.

Drying
Dries easily and well, but is prone to sap stain and should be anti-stain dipped.

Strength
Similar to African mahogany in most strength categories.

Durability
Non-durable.

Working qualities
Saws easily, and works well with all tools. Takes nails, screws, glue, and stains and polishes satisfactorily. It is a good peeling timber.

Uses
Furniture, veneer, plywood, interior trim and joinery, turnery.

ERIMADO

Ricinodendron heudelotii   Family : Euphorbiaceae
Pierre ex Pax.
Syn. *R. africanum* Muell. Arg.

Other names
wama (Ghana) ; sanga sanga (Zaire) ; essessang (Cameroons, Gabon) ; mungenge (Angola).

Distribution
Ricinodendron is a tree typical of the secondary forest, and it is quite common on the site of abandoned farms. It is widely dispersed in tropical Africa from Guinea to Angola, Zaire, Uganda, and other areas of East Africa.

The tree
It is considered to be one of the fastest growing African trees, variable in size ; it may become very large, up to 30m or more tall, and almost 1.5m in diameter, but sometimes it is a small tree only 6m to 10m high. It is usually medium sized however, with a height of up to 21m and a diameter of about 0.75m. The trunk is cylindrical, sometimes with very short buttresses.

The timber
The heartwood is not distinct from the sapwood. It is white or straw-coloured, but often appears greyish because of fungal staining. The texture is rather coarse, and the grain is straight. The wood is very soft and extremely light, weighing between 200 and 350 kg/m^3 when dried.

Drying
No information, but it is reputed to have a high volumetric shrinkage, and not to remain stable when worked.

Durability
Perishable.

Working qualities
Easy to saw, but difficult to plane because of lifting of the fibres.

The assembly of parts is not firm; nails and screws enter easily, but they do not hold well. Unsuitable for painting because of the wood's absorbency.

Uses
It is a good substitute for balsa, or cork, but because of its long, thin-walled fibres, is more suitable for paper pulp or cellulose extraction for rayon or fibre board.

ESIA

Combretodendron macrocarpum　　　　Family: Lecythidaceae
(P. Beauv.) Keay.
Syn. *C. africanum* Exell.

Other names
owewe (Nigeria); minzu (Zaire); abale (Ivory Coast); abine (Gabon).

Distribution
Grows throughout West Tropical Africa from Guinea to Zaire and Angola. It is infrequent in the dry high forests, but fairly common in the wet forest areas, particularly in Nigeria.

The tree
A large tree up to 36m high and about 1.0m in diameter. The bole is straight and cylindrical. It is unbuttressed, but may be swollen at the base.

The timber
The sapwood is yellowish-white, sharply defined from the heartwood, and about 75mm wide. The heartwood is rose coloured when freshly cut, but when exposed to the air it darkens to a reddish-brown. Darker veins or streaks give it a rather speckled appearance. The wood has a strong, unpleasant odour when freshly cut, which disappears on drying.
The wood is hard and heavy and weighs about 800 kg/m^3 when dried. The grain is straight to interlocked, and the texture is moderately coarse.

Drying
Difficult to dry without distortion. The wood dries slowly and is likely to check and split. End-splitting, surface checking, and shakes may be serious. It is improbable that this timber can be

kiln dried satisfactorily from the green condition. It is classified as having large movement values.

Durability
Durable.

Working qualities
Rather difficult to work; saw teeth tend to overheat due to fine sawdust adhering to the packing of circular saws. In planing, a cutting angle of 20° is necessary to prevent tearing of the surfaces. The wood stains and polishes well, but grain filling is usually necessary.

Uses
Heavy or rough construction work, railway sleepers. The unfavourable characteristics of esia prevent its use for more exacting work.

GABOON

Aucoumea klaineana Pierre.   Family: Burseraceae

Other names
okoumé (Gabon); mofoumou, n'goumi (Equatorial Guinea).

Distribution
The natural distribution of gaboon is fairly restricted, being found mainly in Equatorial Guinea, Gabon, and the Congo.

The tree
The tree attains very large sizes and may be 1.0m to 2.5m in diameter at the base.

The timber
Gaboon is one of the most useful hardwoods and is used in large quantities for plywood and blockboard. As it has a fairly close resemblance to African mahogany, it has been known as gaboon mahogany, but since it is unrelated to the true mahoganies the description is misleading and should be discontinued. The colour of the wood is fairly constant at a light pinkish-brown. It is usually straight grained with little figure, though there is a slight stripe when cut on the quarter. It weighs 430 kg/m³ when dried.

Drying
The timber dries well with comparatively little tendency to degrade during the process.

Strength
It is a weak wood with strength properties about the same as for poplar.

Durability
It is not very resistant to decay, but its use being mainly confined to interior work, this point is not of great importance.

Working qualities
The timber works reasonably well with most hand and machine tools, but it is inclined to be woolly, and blunts saw teeth rather quickly. Since its use is mainly for plywood and blockboard, the processes involved in veneer production can be carried out without undue difficulty, and the resultant boards take a fine sheen when scraped or sanded.

Uses
The most important use for gaboon is in the manufacture of plywood, blockboard and laminboard, which are used for a variety of purposes from flush doors to panelling and cabinet work. In the solid it is used commonly as a substitute for mahogany in cabinet work.

GEDU NOHOR

Entandrophragma angolense C. DC., **Family: Meliaceae**
and its varieties

Other names
edinam (Ghana); tiama (Ivory Coast); kalungi (Zaire); abenbegne (Gabon); timbi (Cameroons).

Distribution
It occurs in the semi-evergreen forests from the Ivory Coast to Angola in the west, across to Uganda in the east.

The tree
It is a large deciduous tree often 48m tall with an average

diameter of 1.0m to 1.5m or more. It is sometimes strongly buttressed, the winged buttresses extending as much as 6m up the trunk.

The timber
The heartwood is typically a uniform reddish-brown, but occasional logs are much lighter coloured, sometimes a pale pink not very different from the pinkish-grey sapwood which may be 100mm wide. The heartwood darkens on exposure. The grain is interlocked, but the stripe figure produced on quarter-sawn surfaces is rather irregular and broad. It has a medium texture. The surface is lustrous, more so than sapele, and when fresh, the wood has a slight scent. It is lighter in weight than sapele, weighing about 560 kg/m^3 when dried.

Drying
The timber dries rapidly with a marked tendency to distort.

Strength
It has good strength properties for its weight, but is slightly inferior in this respect to African mahogany and sapele.

Durability
Moderately durable.

Working qualities
Works fairly easily with hand and machine tools, but owing to interlocked grain it has a marked tendency to tear during planing or moulding unless the cutting angle is reduced to at least 15°. It glues, nails and screws well, and takes a good polish if the grain is filled. Decorative veneer can be produced, and the plain veneer is suitable for the manufacture of plywood.

Uses
Gedu nohor has the same uses as for sapele and mahogany, ie, furniture, interior decoration, fittings in shops, offices and ships.

GHEOMBI

Sindoropsis le-testui   Family : Caesalpiniaceae

Distribution
Endemic to Gabon.

The tree
A small to medium-size tree reaching a height of 15m and a diameter of 0.6m to 0.9m with a straight and cylindrical bole, usually unbuttressed.

The timber
The sapwood is white, well defined from the red-brown heartwood which darkens on exposure. The wood contains resin canals, has a generally straight grain and a coarse, but even texture. It weighs from 650–720 kg/m³ when dry.

Drying
Dries easily and well, but logs and stock should be dipped as soon as possible to prevent losses from insects and fungi.

Strength
Similar to dahoma in most strength categories.

Durability
Moderately durable.

Working qualities
Works and machines satisfactorily, and planes to a smooth surface, although the resin sometimes tends to stain the wood. Takes nails, screws, glue, stains and polish satisfactorily.

Uses
Flooring, furniture, veneer, plywood, interior trim and joinery.

GMELINA

Gmelina arborea Linn.   Family : Verbenaceae

Other names
yamane, yemene, gambari ; gmelina is the preferred BS name.

Distribution
Widely distributed throughout India and Burma, the tree has been planted extensively in Africa, particularly in South Africa, Sierra Leone, Ghana, and Nigeria where it is considered one of the most important exotic trees.

The tree
It is extremely fast growing, attaining a height of 30m and a diameter of 0.75m. The form varies with growth conditions, the best results being obtained in deep fertile, moist but well-drained soils in high rainfall districts.

The timber
The sapwood is up to 60mm wide and only slightly distinguished from the heartwood which is creamy white or straw-coloured, often with a pink tinge. The grain is interlocked and slightly wavy, giving a stripe figure on quarter-sawn surfaces, and the texture is moderately coarse. Tension wood is sometimes present. The wood weighs about 480 kg/m^3 when dry.

Drying
Air dries well and fairly rapidly, and is tolerant of high kiln temperatures.

Strength
Although related to teak, it is inferior to that timber in general strength properties being about 17 per cent weaker in transverse strength, 30 per cent weaker in compression parallel to the grain, and some 16 per cent weaker in modulus of elasticity.

Durability
Moderately durable.

Working qualities
Saws easily, and has only a slight blunting effect on cutting edges. Planes and moulds to a smooth finish, but may need reduced cutting angles when knots are present. Although it moulds well, it is too soft for general turnery. Stains, polishes and glues well, and is a good peeler for veneer. Tends to split in nailing. The wood is reported to be very stable in service.

Uses
Light construction, domestic flooring, boat building, furniture, veneer and plywood, interior joinery, carving, pattern making. Early results from African plantations showed the wood to contain a fairly high proportion of knots varying from pin knots to rather large unacceptable knots. Pruning methods have been improved, and with the normal grading for export, gmelina should prove an acceptable addition to the market.

GREVILLEA

Grevillea robusta A. Cunn.   Family : Proteaceae

Other names
African silky-oak.

This is an introduced species which has been extensively planted in Tanzania and Kenya as a shade tree. It is a native of Australia and was formerly exported from there to the UK ; in recent years supplies have been received from East Africa. It should not be confused with Australian silky-oak (*Cardwellia sublimis*).

The tree
Grows to a height of about 30m but is generally considerably branched.

The timber
Somewhat paler in colour than Australian silky-oak (*Cardwellia*), it is a light golden-brown, sometimes with a pinkish tinge, having a marked 'silver grain' on quarter-sawn surfaces due to the large rays. It is straight grained, and moderately coarse textured. Moderately hard, and moderately heavy, it weighs about 580 kg/m^3 when dried. Owing to the fact that the tree is grown in the open to provide shade on coffee and tea plantations, the wood is inclined to be relatively knotty.

Drying
The timber needs care in drying to avoid warping and checking.

Strength
No data are available.

Durability
Probably moderately durable.

Working qualities
The timber works fairly easily although some difficulty may be experienced due to crumbling of the ray cell walls. A cutting angle of 20° gives better results in planing and moulding. Nails and screws well, stains satisfactorily and takes a good polish.

Uses

Grevillea is used for block and strip flooring; its resistance to abrasion is high. It is also used as a substitute for oak for furniture, cabinet work, shop fittings, and panelling, either in solid or veneer form.

GUAREA

Guarea thompsonii Sprague and Hutch.   Family: Meliaceae
and *G. cedrata* Pellegr.

These two species show little differences in technical properties, and it is common practice to market both under the same trade name. Except in special instances this is relatively unimportant.

Other names

G. thompsonii—black guarea, obobonekwi (nekwi means black) (Nigeria); diambi (Zaire).
G. cedrata—white guarea, obobonofua (nofua means white) (Nigeria); bossé, (Ghana); scented cedar (UK).

Distribution

Ghana, southern Nigeria, and Liberia. It is not so common in the Ivory Coast but it is found there as well as in Gabon and Zaire.

The tree

The trees vary in height from 15m in Zaire, to 30m or more elsewhere, with a diameter 1.0m or slightly more above the large buttresses. *G. cedrata* is usually the larger tree.

The timber

G. thompsonii—Pinkish-brown, like a pale mahogany, darkening to a better colour than *G. cedrata*. Straight grain and a silky appearance. Weight about 640 kg/m^3 when dried.

G. cedrata—Pinkish-brown, with a fine texture, and cedar-like scent. Weight about 590 kg/m^3 when dried.

Drying

There is little difficulty in air drying; *G. cedrata* is generally less liable to split and warp. Kiln drying requires care in order to avoid exudation of a clear resin from the wood.

Durability
Both species are considered to be durable.

Working qualities
G. thompsonii—Works fairly easily with both hand and machine tools with only a slight dulling effect on cutting edges. Less woolly than *G. cedrata*, it compares favourably with the denser grades of American mahogany. When interlocked grain is present there is a tendency to pick up in planing and moulding operations and a reduced cutting angle of 20° is recommended. It finishes cleanly and takes a high polish, and also takes nails, screws and glue without trouble.

G. cedrata—Works fairly easily but is inclined to be a little more woolly than *G. thompsonii* and tends to dull cutting edges more readily. Cutting angles should be reduced for planing and moulding. Care is required in polishing as resin may be exuded especially in warm atmospheres.

Uses
Both species are used for the same purposes, ie, furniture, cabinet-making, shop fitting, boat-building, high-class joinery and veneer. Because of the tendency to exude resin, care should be taken when either species is intended for such uses as instrument cases and cigar-boxes.

IDIGBO

Terminalia ivorensis A. Chev.　　　　Family: Combretaceae

Other names
emeri (Ghana) ; framiré (Ivory Coast). Black afara is a name used in Nigeria for the tree. As a timber name it is confusing and should not be used.

Distribution
Occurs in Equatorial Guinea, Sierra Leone, Liberia, Ivory Coast, Ghana, southern Nigeria, in parts of the rain forest and throughout the deciduous forest areas.

The tree
A tall tree with a buttressed trunk attaining a height of over 30m and commonly 1.0m or more in diameter. The buttresses are broad and blunt, but the bole usually is clean and straight, 20m or more above the buttress.

The timber
A plain, pale yellow to light brown coloured wood, sometimes relieved by a zonal figure originating in the growth rings, suggesting plain oak. There is little distinction between sapwood and heartwood, though the latter is somewhat darker in colour. The grain is straight to slightly irregular, and the texture is somewhat coarse and uneven. It is soft to medium hard, and weighs about 560 kg/m³ when dried. The weight is often variable, due to a prevalence of light-weight brittle-heart, particularly in large, over-mature logs. It may vary from 480 to 625 kg/m³ but for general assessment, the average dry weight is as given.

Drying
Idigbo dries readily and well, with little distortion and splitting, and shrinkage is small.

Strength
It has excellent strength properties, being as strong and stiff as English oak in bending, although considerably softer and less resistant to shock loads. It splits easily and has been used in West Africa for roof shingles. When converting large logs the heart should be boxed out as the brittle-heart has very much lower strength properties than the normal wood. In freshly converted stock, brittle-heart may often be recognised by a distinctive pinkish colour which may develop after exposure to light for a few days. Natural compression failures, often referred to as 'thunder shakes' usually accompany brittle-heart.

Durability
Durable.

Working qualities
The timber works easily with most hand and machine tools. It has little dulling effect on cutting edges and a clean finish is obtained in most operations. There is a tendency however, for the

grain to pick up when quarter-sawn material is planed, and a reduction of cutting angle to 20° or less is advisable where smooth surfaces are required. Idigbo turns well and has fairly good nail and screw holding properties and will take glue well; stains effectively and reacts well to finishing treatments.

Uses
A useful utility timber for many purposes. It can readily be converted to rotary-cut veneer suitable for plywood, and because of its stability, ease of working, durability, and attractive appearance, it is useful for fine carpentry, joinery, and construction work. It is suitable for domestic flooring, window and door frames, etc.

The timber contains a yellow colouring matter which may leach under moist conditions and is liable to stain fabrics, and it also contains tannin in sufficient quantity for the wood to become stained if in contact with iron when wet. It is slightly acidic and may tend to promote corrosion of ferrous metals. Suitable precautions should therefore be taken in those conditions of use where the wood might become moist to protect such metal as would be in contact with the wood, or by use of non-ferrous metal.

ILOMBA

Pycnanthus angolensis Warb.   Family: Myristicaceae

Other names
akomu (Nigeria); otie (Ghana); walélé (Ivory Coast); eteng (Cameroons and Gabon).

Distribution
Ilomba is widely distributed in the rain forests of West Africa from Guinea through the Ivory Coast, Ghana, and Nigeria, eastwards to Uganda.

The tree
It is a tall tree, attaining a height of 30m to 36m with a diameter of 0.75m or more. Buttresses are very small or absent, and the bole is straight and cylindrical.

The timber
The wood is greyish-white to dull pinkish-brown when dry, with little distinction between sapwood and heartwood; it has a very disagreeable odour when freshly cut, but this disappears upon drying. The wood is prone to fungal staining if not converted and dried quickly. The grain is usually straight, and the texture is rather coarse. Moderately hard to soft, the wood weighs about 510 kg/m³ when dried.

Drying
Dries with a distinct tendency to split and distort.

Strength
It has only moderate strength, and is inclined to be brittle.

Durability
Perishable.

Working qualities
Easy to saw, and because of the general absence of interlocked grain, relatively easy to plane. It glues and nails satisfactorily, but is difficult to polish, and absorbs too much paint.

Uses
A light-weight timber suitable for plywood core stock, and for general carpentry. It is used as a general utility timber in its countries of origin.

IROKO

Chlorophora excelsa Benth. and Hook f.   Family: Moraceae
and *C. regia* A. Chev.

Other names
odum (Ghana and Ivory Coast); mvule (East Africa); kambala (Zaire); bang (Cameroons); moreira (Angola); tule, intule (Mozambique).

Distribution
C. excelsa has a wide distribution in tropical Africa, from Sierra Leone in the west, to Tanzania in the east.

C. regia is confined to West Africa, where it occurs from Senegal to Ghana. There does not appear to be any significant difference between the timber of the two species.

The tree
C. excelsa attains very large sizes, reaching 45m or more in height and up to 2.7m in diameter. The stem is usually cylindrical and mostly without buttresses. It occurs in the rain, and mixed-deciduous forests.

The timber
When freshly cut, or when unexposed to light, the heartwood is a distinct yellow colour, but on exposure to light it quickly becomes golden-brown. The sapwood is narrow, being about 50mm to 75mm wide, and clearly defined. The grain is usually interlocked and the texture is rather coarse but even, and the wood weighs on average 660 kg/m^3 when dried. Large, hard deposits of calcium carbonate called 'stone' deposits, are sometimes present in cavities, probably as a result of injury to the tree. They are often enclosed by the wood and not visible until the time of sawing, though the wood around them may be darker in colour, thus giving an indication of their presence.

Drying
The timber dries well and fairly rapidly, with only a slight tendency to distortion and splitting.

Strength
Iroko has excellent strength properties, comparing well with teak, though weaker in bending and in compression along the grain.

Durability
Very durable.

Working qualities
Iroko works fairly well with most tools, though with some dulling effect on their cutting edges, especially when calcareous deposits are prevalent. On quarter-sawn stock, there is a tendency for grain to pick up due to interlocked grain, and a reduction of cutting angle to 15° is usually necessary to obtain a smooth surface. An excellent finish can be obtained if the

grain is filled. It takes nails and screws well, and can be glued satisfactorily.

Uses
The timber is of great importance in both East and West Africa. It is valuable for ship and boat-building, light flooring, interior and exterior joinery, window frames, sills, stair treads, fire-proof doors, laboratory benches, furniture, carvings, marine uses such as piling, dock and harbour work, and produces a satisfactory sliced veneer.

IZOMBE

Testulea gabonensis   Family: Ochnaceae

The tree
The tree occurs in West Africa and is about 36m tall, with diameters ranging from 0.9m–1.2m above the thick buttresses. It has a straight, cylindrical bole, commonly from 9m to 18m in length. The distribution is scattered in the dense, mixed, equatorial forests and transitional formations, particularly in Gabon.

The timber
The sapwood is 25mm–50mm wide, and not well demarcated from the heartwood which may be orange-yellow, grey-yellow, or pinkish-yellow, invariably with a greyish hue. The grain is straight, and the texture is very fine and even. Some cells contain a dark gum, and the wood is sometimes figured. It weighs about 800 kg/m^3 when dry.

Drying
Dries fairly well, with little distortion. The sapwood is liable to blue-stain.

Strength
Generally similar to afrormosia in most strength categories.

Durability
Durable.

Working qualities

Works easily with both hand and machine tools, and finishes well in planing and moulding. Glues well, and takes stains and polish satisfactorily, and has good nailing properties, although there is a slight tendency for splitting to occur. It has good slicing properties for veneer.

Uses

Heavy construction, flooring, furniture and cabinets, veneer and plywood, boxes for precision instruments, joinery, including doors and windows, carving, turnery and pattern making.

KANDA

Beilschmiedia spp.   Family: Lauraceae

Other names

bitéhi (Ivory Coast) ; nkonengu (Gabon) ; bonzale (Zaire).

Distribution

Common in the primary forest in Gabon, but widely, although sometimes scattered in almost all the tropical forests of West Africa. Gabon, Cameroons, and Ivory Coast are present producers of kanda.

The tree

A well-shaped tree without buttresses, with a usable bole of 18m to 25m but usually producing commercial logs 6m to 7m in length, with diameters mostly between 0.7m and 0.8m.

The timber

The sapwood varies in colour from pinkish to yellowish, and is clearly defined from the heartwood which varies in colour, according to growth conditions, from pinkish-brown to reddish-brown, to darkish brown. The grain is usually straight, and the texture is medium to fairly fine. Growth ring markings appear on plain-sawn surfaces as rather subdued, brighter lines. The wood has a dull appearance and weighs about 730 kg/m^3 on average, after air drying.

Drying

Difficult and slow to dry, with a definite tendency to check seriously, and for casehardening to develop. Requires care and protection from hot sun during air drying, followed by careful, controlled kiln drying.

Strength
Reported to have good strength properties.

Durability
Durable.

Wokring qualities
Difficult to saw, and has a severe blunting effect on cutting edges due to the fairly high silica content of the wood, while gum may also contribute to this. It planes and moulds well, and is capable of a good finish, and turns well. It can be glued, stained and polished, and has good nailing and screwing properties. Although abrasive, it is said to peel and slice satis-factorily for veneer.

Uses
Joinery, marine uses where available sizes fit the proposed use, and possibly plywood.

LIMBALI

Gilbertiodendron dewevrei   Family: Leguminosae

Distribution
Occurs in west and central Africa where it is found in swampy forests and in dense forests with sandy soil. Also occurs along streams.

The tree
Grows to a height of 18–36m and a diameter of 1–2m. Boles range from 6–21m in length, and are straight, cylindrical, and often without buttresses.

The timber
The sapwood is from 50mm to 75mm wide, paler in colour than the heartwood, which varies from light brown, yellow-brown, to dark brown, often with a red tinge. Cells containing gum are

present. The grain is straight or wavy, rarely interlocked, and the texture varies from fine to coarse. Quarter-sawn stock often has an attractive figure. The wood is hard and heavy, weighing 800–900 kg/m³ when dry.

Drying
Dries reasonably well, but with a tendency to split.

Strength
The general strength properties are similar to those of afrormosia.

Durability
Durable.

Working qualities
Works fairly well, but tends to dull cutting edges fairly rapidly. It planes easily and produces a good finish. Takes paint and varnish well, and can be polished, but ample grain filling is usually required. Holds nails and screws well, but there is a tendency for thin sizes to split.

Uses
Heavy construction, flooring, both light and heavy duty, vehicle bodies, agricultural implements, joinery, sleepers, turnery.

LOLIONDO

Olea welwitschii Gilg. and Schellenb.   Family : Oleaceae

Other names
Elgon olive (Kenya).

Distribution
Kenya, Uganda and Tanzania.

The tree
A large tree, up to 30m high, with a diameter of 0.75m above a buttress. Generally the tree has a straight bole.

The timber
The timber is pale brown, often with a pinkish tinge, and

occasionally with variegated dark brown streaks giving it a very similar appearance to that of the related East African olive (*Olea hochstetteri*). The sapwood is clearly defined and is light yellowish in colour. The grain is straight or interlocked, and the texture is moderately fine. Moderately hard and heavy it has an average weight of 800 kg/m^3 when dried.

Drying
It is a slow drying species with a tendency to check and split if the drying rate is accelerated too much.

Strength
It is reported to have good strength properties, well above average for timbers of the same weight.

Durability
Moderately durable.

Working qualities
The timber is fairly easy to work, both with hand and machine tools, though some dulling of their cutting edges is liable, and the grain tends to chip out in planing and recessing due to the difference in density between the light and dark zones of wood. It is liable to split in nailing and therefore requires to be pre-bored. It stains and polishes well.

Uses
Has been used for heavy construction work, railway sleepers, and furniture in East Africa, but is generally considered a flooring timber in the UK, and for this purpose is classed as having a high resistance to abrasion.

LONGUI ROUGE

Gambeya africana   Family : Sapotaceae

Distribution
Gambeya lacourtiana, or abam, occurs in the dense mixed forest all over Congo-Brazzaville and Congo-Kinshasa.
G. madagascariensis or famelona a grande feuilles, is found in Malagasy.
G subnuda, or longui noir occurs in evergreen forests of central Africa, while

G. africana, or longui rouge, which is perhaps the best of the species occurs also in the Congo. It should not be confused with the longui rouge of tropical America (*Chrysophyllum*).

The tree
G. africana grows to a height of 21m to 30m with a diameter of 0.6m or a little more. The bole may be angular, or slightly fluted, but good specimens are straight and cylindrical, and up to 12m in length.

General characteristics
There is little difference in colour between sapwood and heartwood, the wood being whitish when first cut, turning pinkish-buff, then olive-yellow, and finally, brownish-yellow, often with irregular dark stripes. The wood contains a pale brown-coloured gum, the grain is usually straight, but occasionally is interlocked, and the texture is fine to medium. It weighs about 710 kg/m^3 when dry.

No information on drying is available, but the wood is reported to saw easily and well, to plane and mould very easily, and to produce a first-class finish. It glues well, and takes a high polish. It does not split in nailing, and holds nails and screws well, and slices and peels satisfactorily. It is moderately durable.

Uses
Construction, domestic flooring, vehicle bodies, furniture, handles, sporting goods (the wood is said to be tough and resilient), agricultural implements, veneer and plywood, joinery, carvings and turnery.

MAFU

Fagaropsis angolensis Dale.   Family: Rutaceae

Other names
mfu (Tanzania) ; murumu (Kenya) ; mukarakati (Kenya).

Distribution
Found generally in the semi-evergreen forests of Tanzania and Kenya.

The tree
A medium sized tree up to 24m high and a diameter of 0.6m.

60

The timber
The heartwood is light greenish to yellow-greenish, darkening to dark greenish-grey on exposure; the sapwood is whitish. Terminal parenchyma produces whitish coloured growth lines on longitudinal surfaces. Occasionally, some logs have irregular markings which give rise to dark curls and streaks. The grain is generally straight, and the texture is medium.

Mafu is moderately hard and heavy, weighing about 672 kg/m^3 on average when dried.

Drying
Difficult to dry with a tendency to split, warp and twist.

Strength
No information available.

Durability
Moderately durable.

Working qualities
The timber is easy to work and takes an excellent finish. It turns and moulds well without undue tearing of fibres, but care must be taken when working near the edges of the material to prevent the fibres breaking away. Splits rather badly when nailed if not pre-bored. Bends reasonably well, and can be peeled satisfactorily.

Uses
Flooring, where it is considered to give a moderate to high resistance to abrasion, cabinet-making, furniture, panelling. Has been used in Ethiopia for plywood manufacture.

MAHOGANY, AFRICAN

Khaya spp.   Family: Meliaceae

The name African mahogany covers all species of *Khaya*, although their timbers vary somewhat in character, particularly in weight. The bulk of the timber shipped is produced by *K. ivorensis* and *K. anthotheca*, each with moderately light-weight, pale to medium-red wood, and it is timber of this type

61

which is accepted commercially as African mahogany; East African *K. nyasica* is generally similar. A small proportion of *K. grandifoliola* is moderately light in weight but much of its timber and that of *K. senegalensis* is darker and appreciably heavier than that normally accepted as African mahogany. It has been suggested that such heavy wood should be marketed separately, and the name heavy African mahogany is recommended.

Other names
Khaya ivorensis A. Chev. (West Africa).
Khaya anthotheca (Welw) A.DC. (West and East Africa).
Ghana, Ivory Coast, Takoradi, Grand Bassam mahogany, according to origin (UK); acajou d'Afrique (France); khaya (USA).

K. ivorensis is also known as Benin, Lagos, Nigerian, and Degema mahogany, Lagoswood and ogwango (Nigeria), and ngollon (Cameroons).

K. anthotheca is also known as krala (Ivory Coast); mangona (Cameroons); munyama (Uganda).

Khaya nyasica Stapf. ex Baker f. (East Africa).
Mozambique mahogany, mbaua, umbaua (Mozambique); mbawa (Malawi); mkangazi (Tanzania).

Khaya grandifoliola C.DC. (West Africa). Beninwood, Benin mahogany (Nigeria); grandifoliola (UK).

Khaya senegalensis (Desr.) A. Juss. (West and Central Africa) dry-zone mahogany (General); bissilom (Port Guinea); Guinea mahogany (UK).

Weight when dried (kg/m³)
K. ivorensis	530
K. anthotheca	540

K. nyasica	590
K. grandifoliola	720*
K. senegalensis	800

*Occasional pieces of light-weight *K. grandifoliola* are included with species designated as African mahogany.

Distribution

K. ivorensis occurs in the coastal rain forests of West Africa from the Ivory Coast to the Cameroons and Gabon, including those of Ghana and Nigeria. *K. anthotheca* grows in West Africa in areas with lower rainfall than *K. ivorensis* requires, and is not found in the coastal belt; in East Africa it is confined mainly to Uganda and Tanzania.

K. grandifoliola grows at some distance from the West African coastal belt, in districts of relatively low rainfall.

K. nyasica occurs in East and Central Africa, particularly in Uganda and Tanzania.

K. senegalensis is found in the west from Senegal to Zaire and across the continent to Sudan and Uganda.

The trees

K. ivorensis. Grows to a height of 30m or more with a clear bole 12m to 25m in length above the buttresses, and with a diameter of 1.0m upwards to 2.0m or more. The habit of all *Khaya* species varies considerably with the growth conditions, but the banks of rivers and streams appear to suit the requirements of the species better than drier soils. Thus *K. anthotheca* is usually not such a good shape as *K. ivorensis*, and *K. grandifoliola* is not so tall, and generally has a more crooked growth habit, though it usually attains a larger girth than other species.

K. senegalensis is a smaller tree and not so well shaped as the usual types of commercial mahogany. It grows mainly in the deciduous savannah forests and generally reaches a height of 15m to 24m with a diameter of about 1.0m.

The timber

African mahogany, ie, *K. ivorensis*, *K. anthotheca*, and *K. grandifoliola* (in part).

The heartwood is distinctly pink when freshly sawn, but when seasoned varies in colour from light pinkish-brown to a deep reddish shade; the yellowish-brown sapwood is not always clearly demarcated. The heartwood of *K. grandifoliola* tends to be darker.

The grain is usually interlocked and the texture is of a coarser nature than that of American mahogany. The quality varies with the locality of growth; some localities are said to produce coarse-textured logs with spongy hearts while others are noted for the fine texture and character of their timber. A common feature is the defect known as 'thunder shake' (cross fractures), which are particularly abundant in trees with a soft or 'punky' heart.

K. nyasica from East Africa inclines to a reddish or golden-brown shade.

Heavy mahogany (dry-zone mahogany), ie *K. senegalensis* and *K. grandifoliola* (in part).

The timber of both these species is appreciably denser, and typically darker than ordinary commercial African mahogany, *K. senegalensis* in particular being deep red-brown with a purple tinge. In respect of grain and texture, there is little difference from the characteristics of African mahogany, but *K. grandifoliola* is reputed to be of high quality.

Drying
African mahogany dries fairly rapidly with generally little degrade. Care should be taken to prevent distortion and splitting, and this aspect is of greater importance when drying heavy mahogany.

Durability
All *Khaya* species are considered moderately durable.

Strength
The strength of African mahogany compares favourably with that of American mahogany (*Swietenia*), but is more resistant to splitting. No data are available regarding strength of heavy mahogany although it can be assumed the heavier species are stronger than African mahogany.

Working qualities

The lighter material is easy to work but the heavier species are slightly more difficult. They all have a tendency to pick up on quarter-sawn surfaces, due to interlocking grain, and a reduction of cutting angles to 15° helps to overcome this tendency. All species can be glued satisfactorily, and generally have good nailing and screwing properties. Takes a high polish and a good finish.

Uses

African mahogany is an important timber for furniture, indoor decoration, both in the solid and as veneer, high quality joinery for staircases, panelling, and domestic flooring, boat planking and cabins, banisters and handrails.

Heavy mahogany has similar uses; *K. senegalensis* is said to provide the best surface-finishing of all the African mahoganies and is a popular timber in East Africa for lorry bodies, construction work, and decking in boats apart from the normal uses of furniture etc.

MAKARATI

Burkea africana Hook.   Family: Leguminosae

Other names

siri (Ivory Coast); pinimo (Ghana); kola (Nigeria); mukalati (Malawi); musheshe (Zambia).

Distribution

Widely distributed in tropical Africa, extending to South Africa, chiefly in the savannah forests.

The tree

A fairly small tree 15m to 22m high.

The timber

The heartwood, when first sawn, is brown with tinges of green and grey, but the colour tones down to dark brown or reddish-brown in a short time. The sapwood is paler. Very hard and heavy, but variable in weight from 750 to 1041 kg/m³ (average about 960 kg/m³) when dried. The grain is interlocked, but the texture is fine.

Drying
Reported to dry fairly well, but with some tendency to distort and shake. A mild kiln schedule is advisable.

Strength
A tough, strong wood, harder and stronger in bending than English oak.

Durability
Durable.

Working qualities
Not difficult to saw, but quarter sawn stock tends to pluck out during planing. Requires care in finishing but is capable of taking a fine polish. Should be pre-bored prior to nailing to avoid splitting.

Uses
Heavy construction, bridges, sleepers, fencing, waggon construction, and for tool handles and flooring.

MAKORÉ

Tieghemella heckelii Hutch. and Dalz.   Family: Sapotaceae

Other names
agamokwe (Nigeria) ; baku, abaku (Ghana).

Distribution
It occurs in Sierra Leone, Nigeria, Ivory Coast, Ghana, and Liberia, generally scattered in the moist high forest zone.

The tree
A large tree with a straight cylindrical bole without buttresses. It attains a height of 36m to 45m and a diameter of 2.7m but

since very large trees are reported to be likely to shatter when felled, the exploitable diameter is more usually 1.0m or slightly more.

The timber
The wood is somewhat similar to a close-grained mahogany. It varies in colour from pinkish to blood red or red-brown; the lighter coloured sapwood is usually 50mm to 75mm wide. Some logs are straight grained, but others have a striking, chequered figure and occasionally show streaks of a darker colour. The texture is much finer than mahogany, and the wood is denser, harder and heavier, weighing about 640 kg/m^3 when dried. The surface is distinctly lustrous.

Drying
Makoré dries at a moderate rate and degrade is generally slight. Some distortion due to twisting may occur in some pieces, and some slight splitting tends to develop around knots.

Strength
A tough and stiff timber comparable with American mahogany, but harder and with much greater resistance to splitting.

Durability
Very durable. The timber is recorded as very resistant to attack by termites in Nigeria.

Working qualities
There is a tendency for saws in particular, and other tools in general to become rapidly blunted. The blunting effect increases as the moisture content of the wood decreases, and for material with a moisture content below 20 per cent, saw teeth should be tipped with tungsten carbide. In planing, cutter angles should be reduced to 20° to avoid tearing of quarter-sawn stock. It stains and polishes well, glues excellently, but tends to split in nailing.

Uses
Furniture, and when figured, is suitable for high-class sliced veneer. Used for doors, table-legs, chairs, superior joinery and fittings, laboratory benches, sills, thresholds and flooring, vehicle bodies, textile rollers and general turnery, cladding and panelling.

MALANCATHA

Malacantha spp.   Family: Sapotaceae

Other names
muna. mutunguru, luniondet, chepkebet (Kenya).

Distribution
Found mainly in the mountain rain forests of Kenya.

The tree
A large tree attaining a height of 45m with a clear bole of 27m above a heavily buttressed base.

The timber
The timber, which has an unpleasant odour when freshly cut, is pinkish-brown in colour, often with a wavy grain which produces a fiddleback figure. The grain generally is irregular, and the texture is moderately fine. Fairly hard for its weight, which is about 496 kg/m³ when dried.

Drying
No information available.

Strength
No information available.

Durability
No information available.

Working qualities
It is stated to be difficult to saw owing to the presence of silica. It planes well and takes a good finish and a high polish.

Uses
Malacantha is a popular timber in East Africa for joinery, lorry bodies, furniture, planking and decking in boat-building, and is also used for brush backs.

MANSONIA

Mansonia altissima A. Chev.   Family: Triplochitonaceae

Other names
ofun (Nigeria) ; bété (Ivory Coast) ; aprono (Ghana).

Distribution
Occurs in southern Nigeria, Ivory Coast, and Ghana.

The tree
A medium-sized slender tree, it reaches a height of 30m with an average diameter at maturity of 0.75m.

The timber
Sapwood is whitish, and the heartwood is yellowish-brown to greyish or grey-brown with frequently, a purplish tinge. Both as regards colour and grain, darker-coloured mansonia is similar to American black walnut. The colour, however, varies considerably and no strict comparison can be made between the two timbers. The grain is usually straight and the texture fine and smooth. It is fairly hard, and weighs 610 kg/m^3 when dried.

Drying
Air dries well with little degrade but for splitting of knots and a slight tendency to warp. Kiln dries fairly rapidly and well. Shakes are inclined to extend, and also some distortion in the length may occur. Shrinkage is small.

Strength
Mansonia compares well with black walnut in strength, but is harder, more resistant to shock loads and stronger in bending ; in other categories it is about equal.

Durability
Very durable. The timber is recorded as fairly resistant to termites in Nigeria.

Working qualities
The timber works easily with all hand and machine tools. It is better than American black walnut in cutting, and has less dulling effect on tools. It takes nails, screws, and glue well, and stains and polishes give an excellent finish.

Uses

Mansonia is mostly used as a decorative timber for furniture and is a substitute for walnut (*Juglans* spp.) ; it is also used for cabinet making, interior joinery, pianos, and turnery.

MISSANDA

Erythrophleum suaveolens Brenan.,   Family: Leguminosae
and *E. ivorense* A. Chev.
Syn. *E. micranthum* Harms.

Other names

E. sauveolens and *E. ivorense:* tali (Ivory Coast) ; potrodom (Ghana) ; erun, sasswood (Nigeria).
E. suaveolens : munara (Uganda).
E. ivorense : kassa (Zaire) ; muave (Zambia).

Distribution

The species of *Erythrophleum* occupy an extensive area in Africa. *E. sauveolens* is a mountain species of the semi-humid areas of West Africa, from which it extends at low altitudes to the boundaries of the equatorial forest. *E. ivorense* grows in the dense equatorial forest. In East Africa, both species occur in the savannah and riparian forests. They are common to tropical Africa generally.

The tree

Erythrophleum grows to a height of 28m to 40m and 1.0m to 2.0m in diameter. Rounded buttresses sometimes rise rather high ; the bole is rarely very straight, and under the best conditions are seldom capable of yielding more than four commercial logs.

The timber

The sapwood is narrow, yellowish or greyish in colour, and the heartwood varies in colour according to the locality of growth. The yellow or orange-brown with russet shading in the heartwood is a warm colour, but it darkens in time more or less depending on area of origin. The texture is coarse, and the grain is decidedly interlocked. The wood has a moderately high lustre, is moderately hard to hard, and is very heavy, weighing about 910 kg/m³ when dried.

Drying
The timber air dries slowly. There is some tendency to distort, but the wood can be dried in good condition if care is taken. Kiln drying must be conducted very slowly.

Strength
An extremely strong timber, except in compression when it is only moderately strong.

Durability
It is reported to be very resistant to decay, and resistant to attack by termites and teredo.

Working qualities
A difficult timber to work and saw; planing is often difficult because of interlocked grain, but the wood turns well. The timber can take a fairly good finish and waxes and polishes well.

Uses
Missanda is mainly used in the UK for flooring purposes; it has a high resistance to wear, and is used in schools and other public buildings. It is also suitable for heavy duty flooring in warehouses. It is an established commercial timber in the countries of origin being employed for heavy construction, exterior carpentry and joinery, for gates, decking of bridges, railway ties, harbour work.

MOABI

Baillonella toxisperma Pierre.   Family: Sapotaceae
Syn. *Mimusops djave* Engl.
and *Mimusops toxisperma* (Pierre) A.Chev.

Other names
djave (Nigeria)

Distribution
Southern Nigeria and Gabon mostly.

The tree
A very large tree often attaining a height of 60m and a diameter of 3m.

The timber
The heartwood is rich red or light reddish-brown in colour; the sapwood is pale, and the texture fine. Fairly hard and heavy, it weighs about 800 kg/m³ when dried.

Drying
Dries at a moderate rate and shows little degrade. There is slight distortion, but some twisting may occur. Treat as for makoré.

Strength
No information available.

Durability
Durable.

Working qualities
Works easily but with some dulling effect on cutting edges. A cutting angle of 20° is necessary in planing quarter-sawn material. Glues and nails satisfactorily, and takes a good finish.

Uses
Furniture, cabinet-making, flooring, decorative veneer.

MTAMBARA

Cephalosphaera usambarensis Warb.   Family: Myristicaceae

Distribution
East Africa, principally in Tanzania.

The tree
A large tree, commonly 50m in height, with a straight, cylindrical bole, some 15m to 24m long and 1.2m in diameter above the well-developed buttresses.

The timber
The sapwood is not clearly demarcated from the heartwood which is pale pinkish-brown with a faint orange tint, and darkening with age to a reddish-brown. The grain is usually straight, and the texture is moderately fine and even. The wood has a plain appearance, without figure or lustre, and weighs

about 590 kg/m^3 when dry. It is very similar in appearance to virola (*Virola* spp.) of central and south America, but is usually rather heavier than virola.

Drying
Dries in the open air slowly but well, and also kiln-dries rapidly, but there is a tendency for thin sizes to warp, and for severe case hardening to occur, particularly in thicknesses greater than 25mm. Case hardening can be relieved however, without difficulty.

Strength
For its weight, mtambara is about average in bending, compression, and cleavage, above average in stiffness and shear strength, but rather low in hardness and resistance to impact.

Durability
Perishable. The wood is liable to mildew and sap stain and should therefore be dipped after conversion from the log.

Working qualities
Very easy to work with both hand and machine tools. It can be sanded to a smooth finish, and takes stains and polish quite well. It peels easily for veneer, and takes and holds nails well. It also glues well, but phenolic resins are said to give the best results.

Uses
Interior joinery, furniture, plywood, light construction.

MUERI

Pygeum africanum Hook f.   Family: Rosaceae

Other names
mkondekonde (Kenya).

Distribution
Occurs in semi-tropical rain forests in Kenya, Ethiopia, Tanzania and Uganda.

The tree
A medium-sized tree, occasionally up to 24m high, sometimes with a clear bole extending 15m above a small buttressed base. It has a diameter of about 0.5m.

The timber

The sapwood and heartwood are not clearly differentiated when freshly cut, and are light pink in colour. Upon exposure, the heartwood darkens to light pinkish-brown. The grain is fairly straight, and the texture is medium fine, and even.

The wood is hard and heavy, weighing about 720 to 768 kg/m^3 when dried.

Drying

Reported in Kenya to be a refractory species, liable to split and warp.

Strength

A moderately strong timber, superior to English oak in all strength properties.

Durability

Probably durable.

Working qualities

The timber saws and works well, and planes to a smooth surface. It can be moulded and turns satisfactorily. It stains evenly and takes a high polish. Care is required when nailing to avoid splitting.

Uses

Used in East Africa for lorry bodies, chopping blocks, bridge decking, cabinet-making and furniture.

MUGONHA

Adina microcephala (Del) Hiern.   Family: Rubiaceae

Other names

matumi, mingerhout, mugunya, watermatoemie, mowana.

Distribution

The tree occurs in Tanzania, Mozambique, Rhodesia, Swaziland and eastern Transvaal.

The tree
A medium to large-sized tree, with a diameter up to 1.2m. It also occurs in Kenya where it is only a shrub.

The timber
The sapwood is not clearly defined from the heartwood which is yellowish-brown with darker markings; it darkens on exposure. When freshly cut the wood is very oily and greasy to the touch; the grain is irregular, and the texture very fine.

A hard heavy wood, it weighs from 800 to 1025 kg/m^3 when dried.

Drying
Dries fairly well, but this process should be carried out slowly in order to minimize surface checking.

Strength
No information is available, but bearing in mind its weight and hardness it should prove to have excellent strength properties.

Durability
Very durable.

Working qualities
Reported to be brittle but saws fairly well. Owing to its hardness the timber is difficult to plane although an excellent surface can be obtained. It polishes well, but is difficult to glue owng to the prevalence of oil.

Uses
Used in countries of origin for guide blocks in mining, machine bearings (because of its oily nature), waggon building and heavy construction. Has been used for flooring where it is said to equal rock maple in its resistance to wear.

MUGONYONE

Apodytes dimidiata E. Mey. Family: Icacinaceae

Other names
white pear, pearwood, muchai, wanda, mungaringare, tchela-laka.

Distribution
The tree is widely distributed, and occurs in Ethiopia, Kenya, Tanzania, Central African Republic and in mountainous regions in South Africa.

The tree
A medium-sized tree, evergreen, commonly 15m to 21m high, with a clear bole up to 15m and a diameter of about 0.5m.

The timber
Sapwood and heartwood are not clearly defined; the wood is generally whitish to light brown with a pink tinge when freshly cut, turning greyish-brown on exposure. Generally straight grained, with a fine, uniform texture. The wood is hard and moderately heavy, weighing about 720 kg/m^3 when dried.

Drying
The timber dries reasonably well, and a mild kilning schedule is recommended.

Strength
The timber has medium strength properties, and is reported to be low in resistance to impact.

Durability
Moderately durable.

Working qualities
Easy to work with all hand and machine tools. Takes a good finish and a high polish. Nails and screws well.

Uses
Used in countries of origin for constructional work, joinery, coach-building, turnery and furniture, and owing to its ease of working has been used for carving. It is reported to have a high resistance to abrasion when used for flooring. Should not be used for exterior work without preservative treatment.

MUHIMBI

Cynometra alexandri C. H. Wright.   Family: Leguminosae

Other names
muhindi (Uganda).

Distribution
Uganda, Tanzania and Zaire. It is fairly abundant in the drier parts of tropical rain forests, but it is also found growing in swamps.

The tree
A large tree, attaining a height of 36m and a diameter of 0.75m above the heavy plank buttresses. Trees with a larger diameter, some may be 2m across, are usually found to be unsound and hollow.

The timber
The sapwood, which is 50mm to 75mm wide, is pale brown in colour, clearly defined from the heartwood which is light reddish-brown when freshly converted, darkening on exposure, and has irregular darker markings. A very fine textured timber, with interlocking grain; extremely hard and heavy, weighing about 910 kg/m^3 when dried.

Drying
Dries slowly, especially in thick sizes, with a tendency to end splitting and severe surface checking.

Strength
A very strong timber, twice as strong as European redwood, in bending, compression and shear.

Durability
Very durable.

Working qualities
Hard to work, with a fairly severe blunting effect on cutting edges. To avoid tearing of the grain, a cutting angle of 15° is recommended. Polishes well, and takes a fine finish. It needs to be pre-bored for nailing.

Uses
Because of its high resistance to abrasion is used extensively for heavy-duty flooring, both in strip and block form. In its countries of origin it is used for heavy construction work, eg, bridge-building, mine shaft guides and also for railway sleepers.

MUHUHU

Brachylaena hutchinsii Hutch.   Family: Compositae

Other names
muhugwe (Tanzania).

Distribution
Found in semi-evergreen and lowland dry forests in the coastal belt and occasionally in highland forests of Tanzania and Kenya.

The tree
A medium sized tree, up to 24m high with a diameter of 0.6m The bole is often curved and fluted and therefore it is difficult to obtain timber in large dimensions.

The timber
The heartwood is a fairly dark shade of yellowish-brown, often with a greenish hue. The wood has a sweet scent reminiscent of sandalwood. The wood is hard and dense, generally straight grained, with a very fine, even texture. It weighs about 930 kg/m³ when dried.

Drying
The timber needs to be dried slowly and carefully to minimize hair checks and end splitting. The wood has a low movement classification.

Strength
A strong and stiff timber, but weak in bending.

Durability
Very durable.

Working qualities
Due to its hardness the timber is somewhat difficult to work, and requires pre-boring before nailing.

Uses
Since the timber is available only in short lengths at the present time its main use is for heavy-duty flooring. It has a very high resistance to abrasion, and has proved a good alternative to maple in factory floors.

In its countries of origin muhuhu is used for heavy construction, bridge decking and girders, and railway sleepers. It is exported to India where it has been used in crematoriums as a substitute for sandalwood.

MUKULUNGU

Autranella congolensis A. Chev.   Family: Sapotaceae

Other names
kungulu, kabulungu, kondo fino (Zaire).

Distribution
Fairly widely distributed in the great equatorial forests of Africa, and is reported to be abundant in the southern part of Zaire.

The tree
A tall tree, 30m or more high, with a cylindrical trunk free from buttresses and up to 1.0m in diameter. The trees tend to split on felling, and sometimes are defective at the centre.

The timber
The sapwood is small and greyish, the heartwood red to dark red often marked with streaks of dark red-brown; resembles Cuban mahogany, but the colour is more variable. Hard and heavy, it weighs about 880 kg/m³ when dried. The texture is fine and the grain is usually straight but sometimes interlocked.

Drying
No information available.

Strength
The wood is reported to be extraordinarily tough and resistant to compression, bending, and impact loads.

Durability
Durable, and is said to be resistant to dilute acids.

Working qualities
Saws and planes fairly easily, takes a smooth finish and a good polish. Nails and screws fairly easily, but with a tendency to split.

Uses
Heavy construction, marine work, bridge decking, turnery, flooring, and has been suggested for lining of acid vats by Belgian authorities.

MUNINGA

Pterocarpus angolensis D.C.   Family: Leguminosae

Other names
mninga (Tanzania) ; ambila (Mozambique) ; mukwa (Zambia and Rhodesia) ; kiaat, kajat, kajatenhout (S Africa).

Distribution
Occurs mainly in savannah forests throughout Tanzania, Zambia, Angola, Mozambique, Rhodesia and South Africa.

The tree
A small tree, up to 15m or slightly more, with a diameter of 0.6m. It has a short bole, usually less than 7.5m in length.

The timber
The timber resembles other species of the *Pterocarpus* genus (padauk from Burma, Andamans and Africa) but lacks the reddish colour of padauk, being brown with irregular reddish streaks. It is also softer and lighter in weight than the padauks, weighing about 640 kg/m³ when dried. The sapwood which is rather wide, is oatmeal in colour; the grain is straight to inter-locked, and the texture is medium.

Drying
The timber has excellent drying properties both in air and kiln drying. There is only the slightest tendency for surface checking to occur. The timber dries rather slowly.

Strength
Owing to the varying grain, even in the same log, its strength

is generally lower on average than the values for padauk, being about 30 per cent inferior in stiffness, but it is about 20 per cent more resistant to shock loads, and about equal in bending strength.

Durability
Very durable.

Working qualities
Easy to saw and work, although there is a tendency for inter-locked grain to pick up in planing quarter sawn surfaces; a cutting angle of 20° is therefore necessary. The wood turns well, has good nailing and screwing properties, and takes a good polish.

Uses
Muninga is an attractive timber, suitable for panelling, high-class joinery and furniture. It makes a first-class floor with a moderate resistance to wear, and is a good timber for decorative veneer.

MUSIZI

Maesopsis eminii Engl.   Family: Rhamnaceae

Other names
awuru (Liberia) ; esenge (Cameroons) ; muhunya (Kenya).

Distribution
Extends from Liberia to the Cameroons, through Zaire to north-west Tanzania and into Uganda and Kenya.

The tree
A medium sized tree in West Africa, it attains a height of 18m with a diameter of 0.5m, with a clear bole free from buttresses. It is usually much larger in East Africa, growing to 30m to 42m and a diameter of 1.0m above short buttresses.

The timber
Heartwood olive-brown, becoming russet upon exposure, sapwood whitish to buff coloured. The grain is interlocked and

the texture is moderately coarse. It is light and soft but firm, weighing about 480 kg/m³ when dried. Rather attractive in appearance, with a satin-like lustre.

Drying
Dries rapidly, but with a tendency to split and warp, and to collapse when drying thick material.

Strength
Very similar to European redwood (*Pinus sylvestris*) in all strength properties.

Durability
Non-durable.

Working qualities
Works easily with all hand and machine tools and finishes to a smooth lustrous surface, although there is a tendency to pick up in planing quarter-sawn surfaces. This can be overcome by reducing the cutting angle to 20°. Takes nails and screws well, but requires filling before polishing.

Uses
Internal joinery and light construction. Should be treated with preservative for exterior purposes.

NIANGON

Tarrietia utilis Sprague.   Family: Sterculiaceae

Other names
ogoué (Ivory Coast and Gabon); wishmore (Liberia); nyankom (Ghana).

Distribution
Occurs in the rain forests of Sierra Leone, Liberia, the Ivory Coast and south-west region of Ghana. It is not present in Nigeria, but reappears in the Cameroons and Gabon.

The tree
The average height is 30m with a diameter up to 1.0m; the

bole length, above the arched, plank buttresses is usually no more than 20m. The bole is cylindrical and well formed when the trees grow on well-drained sites, but in swampy areas it is twisted and irregular.

The timber
The heartwood and sapwood are not clearly distinct. The heartwood varies from pale pink to reddish-brown; the sapwood is lighter coloured and about 75mm wide. The grain is often wavy and interlocked, so that quarter-sawn material shows an irregular stripe figure. The texture is rather coarse, and the timber has a greasy feel, due to the presence of resin. The weight is variable, from 512 to 770 kg/m³, and averaging about 625 kg/m³ when dried. Niangon is similar to African mahogany but coarser in texture and denser. The two timbers may also be distinguished by examination of the radial surface (quarter-sawn); in niangon the large rays are conspicuous as dark flecks; in mahogany they are hardly visible. This characteristic gives niangon an attractive figure when quarter-sawn, which is often emphasised by the interlocking grain.

Drying
The timber presents only minor drying problems, and it dries fairly rapidly. A small proportion of the wood may show a tendency to twist. There might be slight end splitting and surface checking, and very slight collapse may occur in a few boards.

Strength
Similar to African mahogany, but in compression, hardness, and resistance to shear and splitting, is appreciably superior and almost equal to oak.

Durability
Moderately durable.

Working qualities
Fairly easy to work. It does not dull cutting edges to any appreciable extent. A considerable improvement in finish is gained by reducing cutting angles to 15°. The timber stains and polishes well but requires a rather large amount of filler; excess of gum in the wood may sometimes create difficulties in

finishing. Takes nails and screws satisfactorily, and generally glues quite well, though the French recommend a preliminary treatment with a solution of caustic soda or ammonia to overcome the resinous nature of the wood prior to gluing or varnishing.

Uses
Niangon is a general-purpose wood for carpentry, joinery and construction.

NIOVÉ

Staudtia stipitata Warb.   Family: Myristiceae

Other names
m'bonda (Cameroons); m'boun (Gabon); kamashi, nkafi (Zaire).

Distribution
Fairly frequent in Gabon and occasionally found in the Cameroons and Zaire.

The tree
A fairly large tree, 22m or more in height, and up to 1.0m in diameter.

The timber
The heartwood is red-brown to yellowish-brown with darker markings; the sapwood is pale yellowish. It is a heavy wood with a fine texture, weighing about 880 kg/m³ when dried.

Drying
No information available.

Strength
No information available.

Durability
Durable.

Working qualities
In spite of its hardness, niové is fairly easy to work, and takes an

excellent polish. Takes and holds nails fairly well. Should be quarter-sawn.

Uses
Cabinet-making and special joinery. It is somewhat heavy to use in the solid for general work, but could be used in veneer form. It is a useful flooring wood, and is also used in Africa for canoe paddles and gun stocks.

'AFRICAN OAK'

Oldfieldia africana Benth and Hook f.   Family: Euphorbiaceae

Other names
angouran, esson, fu, fou, esui, etu.

Distribution
The tree has a restricted range, occurring between Sierra Leone and the western part of the Ivory Coast.

The tree
The tree is very large, often more than 30m tall and 1.2m or more in diameter. The bole is long and clear, with low buttresses and prop roots.

The timber
The heartwood is brown or reddish-brown, and the sapwood which is not sharply defined, is greyish-olive, sometimes with a greenish stain. The wood has a slightly bitter taste. The grain is irregular and often interlocked, and the texture is medium fine. It is a very hard, tough and strong wood, and weighs about 993 kg/m^3 when dried.

Drying
No information available, but it is said to hold its place well in service.

Strength
A very hard and strong timber with properties in all categories superior to those of ekki.

Durability
Very durable.

Working qualities
Difficult to work when it is dry, but it finishes smoothly.

Uses
Used locally for heavy, durable construction, and for keelsons
for boats. It is suitable for constructions subjected to water, eg
bridges, bridge and other decking, floodgates.

This timber, which has no botanical connection with true oak
(*Quercus* spp), was used extensively by the English and
French navies some 200 years ago.

OBECHE

Triplochiton scleroxylon   Family: Triplochitonaceae
K. Schum.

Other names
obechi, arere (Nigeria); wawa (Ghana); samba, wawa
(Ivory Coast); ayous (Cameroons).

Distribution
Obeche is found in most of the countries of West Africa,
especially Nigeria, Ghana, the Ivory Coast and the Cameroons.

The tree
A large forest tree, 45m or more high with extensive sharp
buttresses, rising in some trees 6m or more up the trunk.
Diameter above the buttresses may be nearly 1.5m.

The timber
The timber is creamy-white to pale yellow in colour with little
or no distinction between the sapwood and heartwood; the
former however, may be up to 150mm wide. It is fairly soft, but
firm and fine and even in texture; the grain is often interlocked,
giving a faintly striped appearance on quarter-sawn surfaces,
otherwise there is seldom any decorative figure. The timber is
light in weight, averaging about 390 kg/m^3 when dried.
Brittle-heart is common in large logs.

Drying
The timber dries rapidly and well and with little tendency to warp or shake. The timber is liable to attack by staining fungi and should be piled in stick immediately after conversion.

Strength
Bearing in mind the light weight of the timber, obeche has good strength properties and, when compared with European red-wood, is only about 15 per cent less in maximum bending strength (modulus of rupture) ; in stiffness it is not so good, being about 50 per cent less than redwood.

Durability
Non-durable. The sapwood is susceptible to attack by powder-post beetles (Lyctidae and Bostrychidae).

Working qualities
The comparative softness of the timber makes it very easy to work with both hand and machine tools. It is desirable to use sharp, thin-edged tools to avoid picking up and crumbling in cutting. An excellent finish can easily be obtained and the timber stains and polishes well but requires light filling to produce a high-grade finish. It takes nails and screws well, and has good gluing properties. Obeche peels and slices with reasonable ease.

Uses
Interior joinery, core-stock for plywood, linings of drawers and cupboards, furniture.

ODOKO

Scottellia coriacea A. Chev. Family: Flacourtiaceae
ex Hutch. & Dalz.

Other names
None.

Distribution
Occurs in West Africa from Liberia to southern Nigeria.

The tree
A slender, straight-boled tree up to 30m in height and a diameter usually not more than about 0.5m but occasionally 1.0m.

The timber
Sapwood and heartwood are not differentiated and are whitish to pale yellow or biscuit-coloured with sporadic darker zones. It is in the beech and sycamore class, and shares many of the good properties of these timbers.

Quarter-sawn surfaces show a distinct 'silver-grain'. The grain is usually straight but is occasionally interlocked; texture is fine and uniform. It is fairly hard (slightly softer than beech) and weighs about 640 kg/m³ when dried (compare beech at about 720 kg/m³ and sycamore at about 630 kg/m³).

Drying
There is a tendency in air drying for odoko to check and split; stain may also develop, checks and hair-shakes may develop during kiln drying, and existing shakes tend to enlarge. Warping is not generally serious.

Strength
Odoko has very similar strength properties to home grown beech, except that it is less resistant to shock loads.

Durability
Non-durable, but easily impregnated with preservatives.

Working qualities
Fairly easy to work though with some tendency to flake on quarter-sawn surfaces (owing to the silver-grain); slight brittleness may cause chipping in some operations. A very good finish is obtainable and the timber takes a good polish. It is prone to split on nailing.

Uses
Odoko is a general utility wood for such purposes as domestic woodware, turnery, brush backs, shoe heels and as a general substitute for beech or sycamore. As a flooring timber it has a

high resistance to wear. It is used in Nigeria for cutting boards, models for casts, wooden spoons, bowls, rollers, flooring blocks.

OGEA

Daniellia ogea Rolfe ex Holl.   Family: Leguminosae
and *Daniellia thurifera* Bennett.

As there are other species of *Daniellia* which should not be confused with *D. ogea* and *D. thurifera*, the distinctive name ogea is to be preferred.

Other names
oziya, daniellia (Nigeria) ; faro (Ivory Coast) ; faro, gum copal, copal (Liberia) ; hyedua (Ghana).

Distribution
D. ogea and *D. thurifera* are the most important of the numerous species of *Daniellia* that occur in West Africa. *D. ogea* occurs throughout West Africa in the drier zone of the high forest belt, while *D. thurifera* is more abundant in the wet, high forest area.

The tree
The trees may be up to 30m high and from 1.2m to 1.5m in diameter. The boles are straight, without buttresses, and free of branches for 15m to 20m from the ground.

The timber
The sapwood is usually wide (often from 100mm to 175mm), and greyish or straw-coloured, not sharply distinct from the heartwood which is light golden-brown to reddish-brown, sometimes marked with darker streaks. Texture is moderately coarse, and the grain is straight to interlocked ; planed surfaces have a high lustre. The timber is light and moderately soft, and weighs from 420 to 580 kg/m^3 when dried, the sapwood being appreciably lighter in weight than the darker heartwood.

Compression failures in the form of cross-shakes, thunder-shakes and ruptures may be prominent near the heart-centre. Vertical gum ducts are scattered among the vessels. It exudes some gum which is used for the manufacture of West African gum copal.

Drying
Ogea dries fairly rapidly from the green with little degrade. In thick material there might be slight distortion and collapse, but the degrade is not severe. The wide sapwood quickly develops stain if not dried soon after conversion.

Strength
The strength properties are about the same as those for abura, except in shock resistance and compressive strength, where it is slightly weaker.

Durability
Perishable, and resistant to impregnation with preservatives.

Working qualities
The timber is easy to work with both hand and machine tools. Interlocked grain causes tearing of quarter-sawn material in planing operations; a cutting angle of 20° and sharp, thin cutter knives are helpful in obtaining a smooth surface. The wood nails well and can be glued satisfactorily. It takes stain readily, but requires filling before polishing.

Uses
Light joinery, boxes and crates as a substitute for spruce (it nails well), core veneer for plywood.

OKAN

Cylicodiscus gabunensis Harms. Family: Leguminosae

Other names
denya (Ghana).

Distribution
Okan is common in the rain forests from Sierra Leone to Liberia, the Cameroons and Gabon. It is particularly plentiful in Nigeria and Ghana.

The tree
The tree may be 55m or more in height and 2.5m to 3m in diameter. The usual diameter of commercial logs is about

1.0m or slightly more. The buttresses are rarely more than 1.0m high, and the bole is straight, cylindrical, and without branches for about 24m.

The timber
The sapwood is pinkish and very distinct from the heartwood which varies from yellow to brown with a greenish tinge; on exposure the colour becomes dark red-brown. The grain is interlocked and the texture is coarse, but the surface of the wood is lustrous. It is hard and very heavy, being about 960 kg/m^3 when dried.

Drying
Okan tends to check and distort in drying; it dries slowly.

Strength
Very high strength values, comparable with greenheart and karri, though slightly inferior.

Durability
Very durable. It is recorded in Nigeria as resistant to termites.

Working qualities
In spite of its hardness, okan works quite well, though with some dulling effect on tools, and with a strong tendency to pick up on quarter-sawn surfaces. Planing requires a cutting angle no greater than 10°. Stains and polishes quite well, but is too hard to be nailed without pre-boring.

Uses
Piling, wharf decking, heavy duty flooring, heavy construction.

OKWEN

Brachystegia spp.,   Family: Leguminosae
including *B. eurycoma* Harms.,
B. leonensis Hutch. & Burtt Davy,
and *B. nigerica* Hoyle & A. P. D. Jones.

Other names
meblo (Ivory Coast); naga (Cameroons); brachystegia (Nigeria).

Distribution
West Africa generally.

The tree
The different species of *Brachystegia* are generally considered as forest giants, sometimes reaching 40m in height. Its diameter may reach 2m or more, but probably most mature trees are not greater than about 1.2m in diameter. The trunk is cylindrical with winged buttresses at the base.

The timber
The timber of the different species are similar in appearance ie light to dark brown, but light and dark alternating stripes may be present, and this feature appears to be more prominent in *B. leonensis*. Weight and workability and other properties also vary between the species.

B. eurycoma
Heartwood pale fawn to dark brown. Weight about 640 kg/m^3 when dried.

B. leonensis.
Heartwood light to dark brown, frequently with alternating light and dark stripes. Weight about 705 kg/m^3 when dried.

B. nigerica
Heartwood pale fawn to fairly dark brown, with occasional alternating light and dark stripes and roe figure on radial surfaces. Weight about 705 kg/m^3 when dried.

In all species the sapwood is wide, and up to 150mm usually. The grain is deeply interlocked, and the texture is medium.

Drying
The wood dries fairly well, but slowly, the chief problem is distortion, but there is some tendency to end splitting and surface checking.

Strength
Most strength properties of okwen are similar to oak, but it is harder, tougher, and more resistant to shear than oak.

Durability
All species are probably moderately durable.

Working qualities
Fairly easy to work with machine tools, but generally hard to work with hand tools. The deeply interlocked grain makes smooth finishing difficult in planing and moulding, and the wood is therefore not suitable for high-class finishing treatments.

Uses
General construction that does not require high durability. Owing to its tendency to ring-shake in felling, it is advisable for conversion to be undertaken in country of origin.

Straight grained logs peel well and are technically suitable for veneer and plywood.

EAST AFRICAN OLIVE

Olea hochstetteri Bak.   Family: Oleaceae

Other names
musheragi (Kenya).

Distribution
It is found mainly in the rain forests of Kenya, but also occurs in Tanzania, and to a much lesser extent in Uganda.

The tree
A medium to large sized tree, 27m in height, with an average diameter of 0.6m and has an irregularly shaped bole, rarely exceeding 10m clear.

The timber
The heartwood is buff-coloured, attractively marked with irregular brownish, greyish, and blackish streaks, which give the wood a marbled appearance. The sapwood is pale brown without characteristic marking. The grain is slightly interlocked and the texture is very fine and even. The timber is hard and heavy, weighing about 900 kg/m^3 when dried.

Drying
The timber needs to be carefully air dried since it is somewhat refractory and liable to check and split. It dries slowly, and it is therefore advisable to protect the ends of logs and planks, and to use thin stickers. It can be kiln dried successfully provided no attempt is made to accelerate the drying rate, but internal checking or honeycombing may develop in thick material.

Strength
The timber has excellent strength properties.

Durability
Moderately durable.

Working qualities
Rather difficult to work, but takes a smooth finish and turns excellently. Stains and polishes well, but requires pre-boring before nailing.

Uses
As flooring has a high resistance to wear and is a reliable substitute for maple. Used for furniture, panelling, turnery, tool handles.

OMU

Entandrophragma candollei Harms.   Family: Meliaceae

Other names
heavy sapele (Nigeria); kosipo (Ivory Coast); atom-assié (Cameroons).

The name heavy sapele is confusing and should be discontinued; the description refers to green logs, which tend to sink in water.

Distribution
The tree is found scattered in the dense virgin forests from

Equatorial Guinea to Zaire. It is rather rare in the western part of the area and more frequent in the Congo Basin.

The tree
It can attain large sizes. The bole is either cylindrical or has a pronounced swelling that continues into long, ramified roots. The trunk is very straight and from 20m to 30m tall and a diameter from 0.75m to 2m.

The timber
Sapwood and heartwood distinct; the former greyish-white to pale brown in colour, and from 25mm to 75mm wide. The heartwood resembles sapele, but is darker being reddish-brown, darkening on exposure, and usually with a purplish tinge. The texture is rather coarse and the grain is interlocked to straight. A ribbon figure is visible on quarter-sawn surfaces due to interlocking grain. The rays often contain small silica granules. When dried, omu is about the same weight as sapele, ie 640 kg/m^3.

Drying
Dries rather slowly with a marked tendency to distort.

Strength
Similar to sapele.

Durability
Moderately durable.

Working qualities
Works fairly readily, but is a little more resistant to cutting than sapele. Tends to tear in planing and moulding; cutting angles should be reduced to 20°. Stains readily, and polishes well.

Uses
Since it is less attractive than sapele, its uses are more restricted to high-class carpentry, for example in naval construction. It produces quite good veneer, often with a moiré figure.

OPEPE

Nauclea diderrichii (De Wild. and Family: Rubiaceae
Th. Dur.) Merr.

Syn. *Sarcocephalus diderrichii*
De Wild. and Th. Dur.

Other names
kusia (Ghana) ; badi (Ivory Coast) ; bilinga (Gabon).

Distribution
This tree has a wide distribution in the equatorial forests of
Equatorial Guinea, Liberia, Ivory Coast, Ghana, Nigeria and the
Cameroons.

The tree
A large, well shaped tree, from 35m to 48m tall and 1.0m to
2.0m in diameter at breast height. The trunk is generally without
buttresses, although old trees often have a basal swelling that
extends not more than 1.0m above the ground. The bole is
slender, cylindrical, and free of branches for 20m to 30m.

The timber
The heartwood is a distinctive uniform golden-yellow or
orange-brown colour, clearly differentiated from the pinkish
yellow sapwood which is usually about 50mm wide. The
texture is coarse and the grain frequently interlocked, producing
a striped or roll figure on quarter-sawn surfaces. Lustrous, very
hard and moderately heavy, it weighs about 750 kg/m³ when
dried.

Drying
Needs careful drying, or checks and splits may develop.
Hair-shakes often occur during drying, but warping generally is
not serious. Especially in large sizes opepe dries very slowly, and
it is advisable to use thin stickers when piling.

Strength
An exceptionally strong timber, superior to English oak in all
strength categories except resistance to shock loads or splitting.

Durability
Very durable. Also has high resistance to marine borers.

Working qualities

The timber works with moderate ease in most hand and machine operations and has a reasonably small dulling effect on tool edges. Quarter-sawn material tends to pick up in planing unless a cutting angle of about 10° is employed. An excellent finish can be obtained; when polishing, the grain needs considerable filling, but a high polish is obtainable. The timber tends to split on nailing.

Uses

Piling and decking in wharves and docks, general construction, domestic flooring, waggon bottoms, sills, furniture, cabinet work, interior decoration, decorative turnery.

OVANGKOL

Guibourtia ehie (A. Chév) J. Léon.   Family: Leguminosae

Other names

amazakoué (Ivory Coast) ; hyeduanini, anokye (Ghana).

Note : The vernacular name hyedua is sometimes applied to this species, but more properly it refers to *Daniellia ogea*, and the term should be restricted to that tree.

Distribution

The species is found in the Ivory Coast, Ghana, southern Nigeria and Gabon.

The tree

Ovangkol is a tall tree, attaining a height of 45m and a girth of 2.5m ; it is buttressed to about 4m but above, the bole is usually cylindrical. On older stems there is a tendency for narrow, slightly raised horizontal rings to be formed, a characteristic shared with *Daniellia ogea*, and the reason for the erroneous application of the name hyedua.

The timber

The heartwood is yellowish-brown to chocolate coloured, with grey to almost black stripes, and is similar to 'Queensland walnut' in appearance.

The grain is interlocked and the texture is slightly coarse. It weighs about 850 kg/m³ when dried.

Drying
Dries rapidly and fairly well with only a slight tendency to distort, but care is needed in kiln drying thick stock in order to avoid collapse.

Strength
No information available.

Durability
Perishable.

Working qualities
Ovangkol is an attractive wood, deserving more attention. It appears to be suitable for high-class furniture and joinery, flooring, and turnery, and as veneer it should provide a useful addition to the range of walnut-like woods.

AFRICAN PADAUK

Pterocarpus soyauxii Taub.   Family: Leguminosae

Other names
camwood, barwood.

Distribution
West Africa, particularly Nigeria, Cameroons, and Zaire.

The tree
A medium sized tree between 15m and 30m high and a diameter of 0.6m to 1.0m. Usually has wide buttresses, and the bole is sometimes divided.

The timber
The sapwood is of an oatmeal colour, wide, often up to 200mm, the heartwood varies from blood red to dark brown with red streaks. A hard, heavy wood, weighing between 640 and 800 kg/m³ when dried. The grain is straight to slightly interlocked, and the texture is moderately coarse.

Drying
Dries well, but slowly.

Strength
No information.

Durability
Very durable.

Working qualities
Works excellently and takes a first-class finish.

Uses
Although commonly known as a dye wood, it is an attractive timber suitable for furniture and cabinet-making. It holds its place well after drying and is not liable to warp. It is used for knife handles, carving, electrical fittings, paddles, oars, and agricultural implements in Africa.

PILLARWOOD

Cassipourea malosana (Baker)   Family: Rhizophoraceae
Alston.
Syn. *C. elliottii* (Engl.) Alston

Other names
ndiri (Tanzania) ; musaisi (Kenya).

Distribution
Fairly widely distributed throughout East Africa, mainly in Tanzania, Malawi and Kenya.

The tree
A tall tree, with a cylindrical bole, up to 0.6m in diameter.

The timber
A pale greyish or off-white coloured wood with irregular darker markings, darkening on exposure to greyish-brown or light purplish-brown. Straight grained, with a fine even texture, somewhat like birch in appearance. Moderately hard and heavy ; weight about 770 kg/m^3 when dried.

Drying
The timber needs care, and should not be allowed to dry too rapidly, so as to avoid splitting and warping.

Strength

Although only about 10 per cent heavier than English oak, it is nearly twice as strong in bending, and 50 per cent stronger in compression and shear.

Durability

The timber is reputed to be durable, but not resistant to termites.

Working qualities

Easy to saw and machine, and planes and moulds readily to a smooth surface. Takes a high polish and stains readily.

Uses

Used in countries of origin for telegraph cross-arms, carpentry and building. May prove suitable for turnery, flooring, skis, stretcher poles, etc, or as a substitute for birch and beech.

POGA

Poga oleosa Pierre.   Family: Rhizophoraceae

Other names

inoi nut (Nigeria) ; ngale (Cameroons) ; ovoga (Gabon) ; afo (Equatorial Guinea).

Distribution

Nigeria, Cameroons and Gabon, mainly.

The tree

A large tree, attaining a height of 45m with a diameter of 1.0m or slightly more. The bole is usually about 15m high and above this the trunk forks considerably. The tree produces edible nuts.

The timber

The heartwood is pinkish-red, and the sapwood is narrow and white, tinged with pinkish stripes. The wood is characterised by having numerous very wide rays, giving a 'silver grain' figure when quarter-sawn, which is similar to Australian silky oak.

It is a soft wood with a coarse texture, light in weight and about 400 kg/m^3 when dried.

Drying
No information available.

Strength
Relatively low strength properties, and reported to be weak in bending.

Durability
Non-durable.

Working qualities
Works easily and well, and planes to a smooth surface; takes nails well.

Uses
Cabinet work, shop-fitting, except where strength is a requirement.

AFRICAN PTERYGOTA

Pterygota bequaertii De Wild.   Family: Sterculiaceae
and *P. macrocarpa* K. Schum.

Other names
koto (Ivory Coast) ; kefe (Nigeria) ; awari, ware (Ghana).

Distribution
Found in the rain forests of Nigeria and the Cameroons.

The tree
A medium sized, fairly slender tree above the rather heavy buttresses. It grows to a height of 23m to 30m with a diameter of 0.5m to 0.75m.

The timber
The wood resembles yellow sterculia (*Sterculia oblonga*); there is no distinction between sapwood and heartwood, the wood being cream in colour, sometimes with a greyish tint. The grain is interlocked, and the texture is moderately coarse. Both species of *Pterygota* are lighter in weight than yellow sterculia which weighs 800 kg/m^3 when dried as opposed to

P. bequaertii which weighs 670 kg/m^3 and *P. macrocarpa* which weighs 580 kg/m^3. The wood shows a fleck figure when quarter-sawn.

Drying
Pterygota needs to be dried quickly after conversion in order to avoid fungal staining. Although it dries quite rapidly, there is a distinct tendency for surface checking to occur.

Strength
Similar to European ash in most strength properties, but is inferior to that wood in toughness, hardness, and especially in resistance to splitting.

Durability
Non-durable.

Working qualities
Easy to work provided cutting edges are kept sharp; there is a tendency for quarter-sawn surfaces to tear in planing and moulding, and a reduction of cutting angle to 20° helps to avoid this. The timber can be glued satisfactorily, nailed reasonably well, and if the grain is filled can be polished to a good finish.

Uses
Core stock for plywood manufacture, or as a backing veneer for panels. Veneer must be handled carefully since dry veneer tends to split very easily. Interior joinery, boxes, crates.

RAPANEA

Rapanea rhododendroides (Gilg.) Mez.   Famliy: Myrsinaceae

Other names
mlimangombe (Tanzania) ; mugaita (Kenya).

Distribution
Occurs in the rain forests of Tanzania and Kenya at elevations of 1200m to 2700m.

The tree
A small to medium sized tree up to 20m but sometimes reaching a height of 27m with a diameter of 0.5m or slightly more. The trunk is often irregular in shape.

The timber
The wood is pinkish when freshly cut, darkening slightly on exposure. The grain is generally straight but with a tendency to spiral, and the texture is medium. The numerous large rays produce a 'silver grain' figure on quarter-sawn surfaces similar to that of Australian silky oak. Hard and heavy, the wood weighs about 910 kg/m³ when dried.

Drying
The timber should be dried slowly to avoid checking and warping.

Strength
No information available.

Durability
Non-durable.

Working qualities
Fairly hard to saw, but takes a good finish and good polish. Difficult to nail.

Uses
Cabinet-making, furniture and panelling.

SAPELE

Entandrophragma cylindricum Sprague.   Family: Meliaceae

Other names
sapelewood (Nigeria); aboudikro (Ivory Coast); sapelli (Cameroons).

Distribution
It is found in the rain forests of West Africa from the Ivory Coast through Ghana and Nigeria to the Cameroons, and it extends eastwards to Uganda and Tanzania.

The tree
A very large tree with cylindrical bole and small or no buttresses. Grows to a height of 45m or more, and a diameter at breast height of 1.0m or slightly more.

The timber
The sapwood is pale yellow or whitish, the heartwood pinkish when freshly cut, darkening to typical mahogany colour of reddish-brown. Sapele is characterised by a marked and regular stripe, particularly pronounced on quarter-sawn surfaces. Occasionally mottle figure is present. It is fairly close textured, and the grain is interlocked. It is harder and heavier than African mahogany, weighing about 640 kg/m³ when dried. It has a pronounced cedar-like scent when freshly cut.

Drying
The timber dries rapidly with a marked tendency to distort. Quarter-sawn material is less liable to degrade in drying.

Strength
Sapele is much harder than African or American mahogany, and in resistance to indentation, bending strength, stiffness, and resistance to shock loads, is practically equal with English oak.

Durability
Moderately durable.

Working qualities
Works fairly well with hand and machine tools, but the interlocked grain is often troublesome in planing and moulding, and a reduction of cutting angle to 15° is needed to obtain a good finish. It takes screws and nails well, glues satisfactorily, stains readily, and takes an excellent polish.

Uses
Constructional and decorative veneer, furniture, cabinet-making, shop-fitting, boat-building, panelling, flooring, joinery.

AFRICAN SATINWOOD

Fagara macrophylla Engl.   Family: Rutaceae

Fagara heitzii Aubrev. & Pellegr. produces the olon of West Africa.

Other names
F. macrophylla; olonvogo, olon dur (France and Gabon).
F. heitzii; olon, olon tendre (France and Gabon).

Distribution
F. macrophylla has a wide range throughout West Africa from Sierra Leone to Angola, and east into Kenya, Uganda, and Tanzania. *F. heitzii* is restricted to West Africa.

The tree
Fagara macrophylla is a species assuming many different forms from one end to the other of its range in the equatorial forest. It is characteristic of the secondary brush area in the Ivory Coast. where it is rarely more than 500mm in diameter. In the secondary forest of Zaire, the tree attains a height of 30m with a diameter of 1.5m.

The timber
The heartwood and sapwood of *Fagara* spp., are not well differentiated. The sapwood is yellowish-white, and the heartwood is almost saffron yellow, sometimes veined or mottled. The grain is interlocked, and the texture is medium to fine. The wood is sweet-scented when freshly cut. *F. macrophylla* weighs from 720 to 880 kg/m^3 when dried, and *F. heitzii*, which produces milder timber, weighs between 560 and 640 kg/m^3.

Drying
Dries fairly well; requires care if surface checking is to be avoided.

Strength
The timber is reported to be very strong and tough.

Durability
Durable.

Working qualities
Moderately difficult to work, and care is needed to prevent

picking-up on quarter-sawn surfaces due to interlocked grain. Takes a fine polish.

Uses
Could be used for furniture and joinery; it is used in its countries of origin for panelling, furniture, and cabinet-making.

STERCULIA, BROWN

Sterculia rhinopetala K. Schum.   Family: Sterculiaceae

Other names
wawabima (Ghana); aye lotofa (Nigeria); red sterculia (UK).

Distribution
Occurs in the rain forests of West Africa from Ghana to southern Nigeria and the Cameroons.

The tree
Grows to a height of 30m with a diameter of about 1.0m or slightly less. The tree has narrow buttresses which extend up the trunk for about 3.0m.

The timber
The sapwood is commonly 38mm to 62mm wide, straw-coloured, and sharply defined from the heartwood which varies in colour from yellowish to a reddish, or reddish-brown. The grain is sometimes straight, but more commonly is interlocked; the texture is rather coarse. Hard and moderately heavy, it weighs about 830 kg/m^3 when dried.

Drying
Dries slowly and needs care to avoid degrade, having a tendency to cup and check.

Strength
Similar to ash, but heavier, and with the exception of resistance to shearing and splitting, is slightly stronger.

Durability
Moderately durable.

Working qualities
Rather woolly to work with a tendency to spring. Interlocked grain causes little tearing in planing and moulding. Tends to split when nailed and can be stained and polished satisfactorily but requires filling.

Uses
Interior joinery and construction. In Nigeria, selected logs are used to produce veneer for plywood manufacture, and flooring blocks are also produced.

STERCULIA, YELLOW

Sterculia oblonga Mast.   Family: Sterculiaceae

Other names
okoko (Nigeria) ; eyong (Cameroons) ; white sterculia (UK).

Distribution
Yellow sterculia is distributed throughout the high forest zone of Nigeria and the Cameroons where it is more frequent in the deciduous forests, but the trees attain larger sizes in the rain forest.

The tree
The trees are 24 to 30m tall and 0.75m to 1.0m in diameter. The bole is free of branches for 15m to 20m and is straight and cylindrical. Buttresses extend sharply up to about 3.5m.

The timber
The heartwood is yellowish-white to pale yellow-brown ; the sapwood is not distinct and may be 100mm to 200mm wide. The grain is somewhat interlocked, and the texture is moderately coarse. The wood has a harsh feel. When cut on the quarter, it shows an oak-like silver grain caused by the large rays. It has a disagreeable odour when freshly cut that disappears after drying ; moderately hard and heavy, it weighs about 800 kg/m^3 when dried.

Drying
Dries slowly and needs care to avoid degrade. It has a marked

tendency to surface checking and end splitting, and cupping may be a serious defect.

Strength
Compares reasonably with ash, but is superior in bending, stiffness and crushing strength; it is appreciably weaker however, in toughness, hardness, shear and splitting strength.

Durability
Non-durable.

Working qualities
Easy to saw and work, but requires sharp cutting edges, and a reduction of cutting angle to 20° to avoid tearing out in planing. Stains and polishes easily, glues reasonably well, and takes nails well, but with a tendency to splitting.

Uses
Its poor drying properties and low natural durability renders it doubtful for furniture and good-class joinery. Suitable for light interior construction.

TCHITOLA

Oxystigma oxyphyllum (Harms) Leon   Family: Leguminosae
Syn. *Pterygopodium oxyphyllum* Harms.

Other names
lolagbola (Nigeria); kitola (Zaire); tola, tola manfuta, tola chimfuta, chanfuta (Angola).

This wood should not be confused with agba (*Gossweilero-dendron balsamiferum*), also sometimes known as tola, tola branca, white tola, etc.

Distribution
Cameroons, Zaire, and Angola.

The tree
A large tree attaining a height of 45m and a diameter up to 2m, with a clean bole above slight buttresses.

The timber

The timber possesses three distinct zones: i. an outside sapwood, which is very gummy and freely exudes a copal-like, cedar-scented gum, the wood being pale yellow in colour; ii. an inside sapwood, also very gummy, but pale reddish in colour, and iii. heartwood in which the gum is present but not in such great quantity. Dark gum-rings give an almost walnut-like appearance to the timber with well-marked and striking black and pale yellow stripes. The wood is moderately heavy, weighing about 610 kg/m^3 when dried. The grain is variable, from straight to interlocked, and the texture is medium.

Drying

Dries easily, but gum exudation is a problem.

Strength

French sources of information state that mechanically it is a soft, pliable wood which, by reason of its known powers of resistance to breaking, is classed among the large number of tropical woods having a high axial compression strength, and certainly in the highest category for static flexibility. To sudden impact however, its resistance is below average. Its resistance to splitting and tension is average.

Durability

Durable.

Working qualities

The presence of gum chokes up tools, and hampers good finishing.

Uses

The heartwood might be used for decorative work, but the timber is generally too gummy for general use.

'RHODESIAN TEAK'

Baikiaea plurijuga Harms.   Family: Leguminosae

Other names

Zambesi redwood (Zambia); umgusi, mukushi, mukusi (Rhodesia).

Distribution

Zambia and Rhodesia, in open forests, scattered, but sometimes gregarious.

The tree
A small to medium-sized tree, up to 15m in height and 0.75m in diameter, with a clear bole varying from 3m to 4m in length.

The timber
The heartwood is reddish-brown sometimes marked with irregular black lines or flecks, and sharply defined from the lighter coloured narrow sapwood. The grain is straight to slightly interlocked, and the texture is fine and even, giving a smooth, hard surface. The weight is about 960 kg/m^3 in the dried condition.

The wood should not be confused with true teak (*Tectona grandis*).

Drying
The timber dries slowly, and with care should not warp or split excessively.

Strength
A heavy, hard timber about 30 per cent harder than rock maple. Other strength properties have not been determined.

Durability
Very durable.

Working qualities
Rather difficult to work; it has an appreciable dulling effect on cutting edges. A good finish is obtained in planing and moulding if the cutting angle is reduced to 20°. The timber turns excellently, and polishes well.

Uses
Its handsome appearance and high resistance to wear makes it an ideal flooring timber, especially for heavy-duty purposes. It is usually available in block form. It is used locally for furniture, waggon building, and sleepers.

TETRABERLINIA

Tetraberlinia tubmaniana Family: Leguminosae
J. Léon.
Syn. *Dideletia* spp.
and *Monopetalanthus* spp.

Other names
ekop.

Distribution
Western province of Liberia, where it is very common in the heavy rainfall areas.

The tree
A large, tall, straight tree, without buttresses, reaching a height of 36m or more, with a diameter generally not exceeding 1.2m at maturity.

The timber
The sapwood is light coloured with a pinkish tinge, and distinct from the reddish-brown heartwood. The wood has a lustre, is moderately coarse textured, and has an attractive grain pattern. Moderately hard, it weighs about 625 kg/m³ when dried.

Drying
No information available.

Strength
It has excellent strength properties, comparing favourably with iroko, but somewhat superior to that timber in modulus of rupture and modulus of elasticity.

Durability
Data are incomplete on this timber but indicate that it will be rated as **non-durable** or **moderately durable**. The Building Research Establishment, Princes Risborough Laboratory, is undertaking trials with this species which should establish the correct UK classification.

Working qualities
No potential difficulties in planing, shaping or turning, and the wood works well with hand tools. Sliced veneer can be produced satisfactorily. The wood takes polish quite well.

Uses
Furniture, cabinet-making, joinery, veneer.

UTILE

Entandrophragma utile Sprague.   Family Meliaceae

Other names
sipo (Ivory Coast) ; assié (Cameroons).

Distribution
Utile has a wide natural distribution in tropical Africa. It occurs in the Ivory Coast, in the Cameroons, and in Liberia, Gabon and Uganda. The tree grows chiefly in the moist, deciduous high forest.

The tree
The tree may be up to 45m tall and 2m in diameter above the base. The bole is straight, cylindrical, and free of buttresses, and may be 21m to 24m long.

The timber
The heartwood and sapwood are distinct; the heartwood is pale pink when freshly cut, darkening on exposure to reddish-brown. It closely resembles the related sapele, both in appearance and properties, but is more open in texture due to the larger pores, and generally lacks the cedar-like odour of sapele. The interlocked grain produces a broad ribbon-stripe, often wider and more irregular than that of sapele. It weighs about 660 kg/m^3 when dried.

Drying
Utile dries moderately slowly with a distinct tendency for distortion in the form of twist to occur, and original shakes to extend. In general however, distortion is not severe.

Strength
Its strength properties are similar to those of American mahogany.

Durability
Durable.

Working qualities
Works rather well, but with a slight blunting effect on cutting

edges. A cutting angle of 15° will reduce the tendency for the interlocked grain to tear during planing and moulding. Takes stain and glue well, and polishes well after filling.

Uses
Utile is used for the same purpose as sapele, ie, furniture, cabinets, joinery, shop-fitting, boat-building, as veneer for plywood, and for decoration.

'AFRICAN WALNUT'

Lovoa trichilioides Harms.   Family: Meliaceae
Syn. *L. klaineana* Pierre ex Sprague

Other names
dibétou, noyer de Gabon, eyan, dilolo (France) ; apopo, sida (Nigeria) ; bombolu (Zaire). In the USA it is known as lovoawood, tigerwood, alonawood and Congowood. It is not a true walnut ie *Juglans* spp.

Distribution
Nigeria, Ghana, Cameroons, Zaire, Gabon.

The tree
It is a tall tree reaching 36m to 39m in height, 1.2m diameter, having a cylindrical bole with a small buttressed or fluted base. Frequently has a clean bole of 18m or more.

The timber
It is of a golden brown colour, marked with black streaks (caused by secretory tissue or 'gum lines'), which have given it the name 'walnut'. When planed the surface is distinctly lustrous. The sapwood is narrow, buff or light brown in colour and normally sharply defined from the heartwood, although a narrow transitional area is sometimes seen. It belongs to the mahogany family and is very similar in many respects to African mahogany. It has usually interlocked grain, giving a marked 'stripe' when cut on the quarter. It averages about 560 kg/m³ when dried.

Drying
Its drying properties are fairly good, although existing shakes may extend slightly and some distortion occur.

Strength
For its weight the strength of the timber is good, and is equal to American black walnut in hardness and in compression along the grain.

Durability
It is only moderately resistant to decay, and is subject to damage by ambrosia beetles and longhorn beetles. The sapwood may be attacked by powder-post beetles (Bostrychidae and Lyctidae).

Working qualities
It works fairly easily with most tools, but tends to pick up on quarter sawn stock due to interlocked grain, and a cutting angle of 15° should be used. Hand turning needs care, and sharp tools to avoid tearing ; in the same way drills need to be sharp or the fibres will tend to tear out at the bottom of the drill hole.

The timber is fairly easy to nail, but with some tendency to split. An excellent finish can be obtained by sanding and scraping and, when filled, a fine finish can be produced.

Uses
Furniture, cabinet-making, billiard tables, panelling, veneer, joinery, chairs, gun butts and sometimes for flooring.

WENGE

Millettia laurentii De Wild.   Family: Leguminosae

Other names
palissandre du Congo, dikela (Zaire).

Distribution
Mainly found in Zaire, but an associated species, *M. stuhlmannii* occurs in East Africa. It is known as panga panga, and its general appearance and characteristics closely resemble wenge.

The tree
Medium-sized tree, 15m to 18m in height with a diameter up to 1.0m.

The timber
Sapwood whitish, heartwood dark brown with fine, close blackish veining, giving the wood a handsome appearance. A very hard and heavy wood, it weighs about 880 kg/m³ when dried (panga panga is slightly lighter in weight at 800 kg/m³). Straight grained, it has a rather coarse texture.

Drying
Dries slowly and requires care if surface checking is to be avoided.

Strength
The wood is stated to have good resistance to bending and to shock.

Durability
Durable.

Working qualities
Reported to be easy to work, but difficult to polish.

Uses
Like panga panga, it is probably best suited to flooring, although the appearance is rather dark. Wenge produces good, decorative veneer suitable for furniture and interior decoration.

ZEBRANO

Brachystegia fleuryana Chev.   Family: Leguminosae

Other names
zebra wood (UK) ; zingana (Gabon and Cameroons).

Distribution
Gabon and Cameroons.

The timber
A decorative wood, light gold in colour, with narrow streaks of dark brown to almost black. The surface is lustrous, and the texture somewhat coarse. The wood is hard and heavy.

Working qualities
Zebrano is mostly used as a veneer, usually as decorative banding. The veneer is sliced, and quarter cut in order to avoid buckling due to the alternating hard and soft grain. The veneer must be glued with care, and should be treated with clear filler before polishing. Finishes well on belt sander.

PART II SOFTWOODS

Africa has very few indigenous conifers and these are restricted to the Mediterranean region, the high mountains of Central and Eastern Africa, and South Africa. A few genera have been introduced into East and South Africa, but of the total forest land of Africa, no more than about one per cent consists of coniferous species.

CYPRESS

Cupressus spp.   Family: Cupressaceae
mainly *C. macrocarpa* Gord.

The principle species grown in East Africa are *C. lusitanica* Mill. (*C. lindleyi*) and *C. macrocarpa* Gord., the latter species is a native of North America, and has been extensively planted in both East and South Africa. The Mediterranean cypress, *C. sempervirens* Linn. has not so far contributed to shipments of cypress to the United Kingdom which generally has been from East Africa.

The tree
Under favourable conditions attains a height of about 30m with a bole of 0.6m to 1.0m.

The timber

The heartwood is yellowish-brown to pinkish-brown usually distinct from the paler sapwood, which is about 50mm to 100mm wide. The grain is usually straight and the texture fine and fairly even; the growth rings are marked by a narrow band of latewood, but are not conspicuous. When dried, the timber weighs about 470 kg/m^3 and has a slight cedar-like odour. It is strong for its weight, and is classified as durable.

Working Qualities

Works readily with machine and hand tools with little dulling effect on cutting edges, but knots, usually frequent, can be troublesome. The timber takes nails well, and gives satisfactory results with the usual finishing treatments.

Uses

Cypress is a strong durable softwood for constructional work, especially where the timber is in contact with the ground, or for external work generally.

'PENCIL CEDAR, EAST AFRICAN'

Juniperus procera Hochst.   Family: Cupressaceae
ex. A. Rich

Distribution

African pencil 'cedar' occurs in East Africa, mainly in Kenya, Uganda, Tanzania, and Ethiopia, in the high elevation forests.

The tree

Generally attains a height of 24m to 30m with a diameter of about 1.5m sometimes reaching larger sizes up to 2.4m or even more. It has a tapered trunk and heavily fluted butt.

The timber

The timber is similar to the well known Virginian pencil 'cedar' (*Juniperus virginiana*), being moderately heavy, reddish-brown in colour, fine textured and characterized by its 'cedar' scent, and fine whittling qualities. The average weight of the dried timber is about 580 kg/m^3 which is slightly heavier than for the American species.

Drying
The timber has a marked tendency towards fine surface checking during drying, especially in thick sizes which also tend to end-split. Should be considered a slow-drying timber.

Durability
The timber is naturally resistant to decay, and is reputed to be immune to Bostrychid attack, and the heartwood to termite attack.

Working qualities
Works easily with all machine and hand tools and normally has very little dulling effect on tool edges, but occasionally logs may have hard patches of abrasive material. An excellent finish can be obtained but cutting edges should be sharp; requires care in screwing, and is liable to split when nailed. The timber can be glued satisfactorily, and good results are obtainable with the usual finishing treatments.

Uses
The principal use is for pencil slats. In East Africa it is used for carpentry, joinery and furniture.

PODO

Podocarpus spp.   Family: Podocarpaceae
principally *P. gracilior* Pilg.,
P. milanjianus Rendle,
and *P. usambarensis* Pilg.

Other name
yellowwood (South Africa).

Distribution
P. gracilior occurs at altitudes of 1200m to 2700m in Kenya, Uganda and Ethiopia, and to a lesser extent in Tanzania. *P. milanjianus* is widely distributed in Kenya at altitudes of 2100m to 3000m and is also found in Uganda, and southward through parts of Tanzania and Zambia and Rhodesia. *P. usambarensis* is found at lower altitudes in Kenya and Tanzania.

The tree
These species attain a height of 30m or more, with diameters averaging 0.75m although *P. gracilior* is sometimes of quite large diameter.

The timber
These species are all similar in appearance; the wood is generally a light yellowish-brown with little distinction between sapwood and heartwood. It is straight grained and of uniform texture, is non-resinous and without odour, and there are no clearly defined growth rings. The weight is similar to European redwood being about 510 kg/m^3 when dry.

Drying
Podo dries fairly rapidly with a pronounced tendency to distort, and should therefore be weighted at the top of the pile, or restrained by mechanical means in order to reduce distortion. It is also liable to split and check, and if compression wood is present, some longitudinal shrinkage can be expected.

Durability
Non-durable and permeable. Non-resistant to attack by the longhorn beetle (*Oemida gahani*), both in the forest and in timber after conversion.

Working qualities
Podo works easily with all hand and machine tools provided reasonable care is taken to prevent breaking out at the exit of the tool in boring, mortising, etc, because of the brittle nature of the timber. It turns, planes, and moulds to a good finish, glues satisfactorily, and takes varnish, polish and paint quite well. Some difficulty is often encountered in staining due to non-uniform penetration. It holds screws firmly, but tends to split in nailing.

Uses
Interior joinery and fittings. *P. gracilior* is reported to be suitable for good quality plywood.

RADIATA PINE

Pinus radiata D. Don   Family: Pinaceae
Syn. *Pinus insignis* Dougl. ex Loud

Other names
insignis (South Africa), Monterey pine (USA).

The tree
Although the natural distribution of this species is limited to a narrow belt on the southern Californian coast, it has been widely planted in South Africa and elsewhere in the southern hemisphere. In its natural habitat it usually grows to a height of 15m to 18m but in the southern hemisphere it tends to grow fast, reaching a height of 21m to 25m in 25 to 30 years, usually with a diameter of 0.3m to 0.6m.

The timber
The pale coloured sapwood is commonly 75mm to 150mm wide, clearly distinct from the pinkish-brown heartwood. The growth rings, although mostly wide and distinct show rather less contrast between early-wood and late-wood than those of Scots or Corsican pine, consequently the texture is relatively uniform. The average weight of the dried timber is about 480 kg/m^3.

Drying
With care the timber dries with little degrade, however where spiral grain is present, appreciable warping may occur.

Durability
Non-durable.

Working qualities
The timber works reasonably well and clear material has little dulling effect on cutting edges. It planes to a smooth clean finish provided cutting edges are thin and sharp. Dull, or thickened cutters tend to tear the wide zones of soft early-wood and around knots. The timber can be glued satisfactorily.

Uses
General construction, joinery, crates and boxes, and is suitable for pulp for kraft paper.

THUYA

Tetraclinis articulata Mast.   Family: Cupressaceae

Distribution
North Africa and Malta.

The tree
A small evergreen tree or shrub of handsome pyramidal outline like *Cupressus*, occurring in North Africa mainly in Algeria and Morocco. *Tetraclinis* should not be confused with western red cedar (*Thuja plicata*). Although botanically related to both *Cupressus* and *Thuja*, *Tetraclinis* differs in that the cones only have four scales.

The timber
The colour of the wood is yellowish-brown red. The grain is rather soft, and the timber possesses an aromatic scent.

Uses
Because of the generally twisted growth characteristics, thuya is generally presented to the market in the form of burrs which are used in the manufacture of small decorative items.

USE GUIDE FOR AFRICAN TIMBERS

AGRICULTURAL IMPLEMENTS
afrormosia; afzelia; celtis, African (as a substitute for ash); difou; iroko; limbali; padauk, African.

BATTERY AND ACCUMULATOR BOXES
abura; mukulungu.

BOAT AND SHIP CONSTRUCTION
Decking agba; afrormosia; gmelina; guarea; iroko; mahogany, African; malacantha; mueri; sapele; utile.
Framing guarea; mahogany, African; 'oak, African'.
Keels and stems afzelia; danta; 'oak, African'.
Paddles niové; padauk, African.
Planking agba; afrormosia; danta; gmelina; guarea; mahogany, African; makoré; malacantha; sapele; utile.
Superstructures agba; afzelia; afrormosia; iroko.
Veneers for moulding agba; makoré; sapele; utile.

BOXES AND CRATES
alstonia; ilomba; ogea (substitute for spruce); pterygota; radiata pine.

CONSTRUCTION
Heavy afzelia; albizia (heavy); dahoma; difou; ekki; esia; izombe; limbali; loliondo; makarati; missanda; mueri; muhuhu; 'oak, African'; okan; opepe.
Light afara; agba; akossika; albizia (light); camphorwood; gmelina; guarea; longui rouge; mtambara; musizi; niangon; ogea; okwen; radiata pine; sterculia, brown; sterculia, yellow; cypress (exterior).

DOORS (SOLID)
abura; afara; afrormosia; afzelia; agba; camphorwood; cypress, gedu nohor; gmelina; guarea; idigbo; iroko; izombe; mahogany, African; makoré; sapele; utile.

FANCY GOODS
bubinga; ebony; olive; ovangkol; padauk, African; 'teak, Rhodesian'; thuya (Burr); zebrano.

FLOORING

abura
afrormosia
afzelia
agba
akossika
ayan
banga wanga
camphorwood
celtis, African
dahoma
danta
difou
ekaba
ekki
gmelina
gedu nohor
gheombi
grevillea
guarea
idigbo
igaganga
iroko
izombe
limbali
loliondo
longui rouge
mafu

mahogany, African
makarati
makoré
missanda
moabi
mugonha
mugonyone
muhimbi
mukulungu
muninga
niové
odoko
okan
ollem
olive
opepe
ovangkol
ozigo
panga panga
safoukala
sapele
sterculia, brown
'teak, Rhodesian'
utile
walnut, African
wenge

FURNITURE AND CABINET WORK

abura
afara
afrormosia
afzelia
agba
akossika
aningeria
avodiré
ayan
berlinia
camphorwood

celtis, African
cordia
danta
difou
ekaba
ekebergia
ekop
ekoune
gaboon
gedu nohor
gheombi

Furniture and cabinet work (cont.)

grevillea
guarea
idigbo
iroko
izombe
longui rouge
mafu
mahogany, African
makoré
malacantha
mansonia
moabi
mtambara
mueri
mugonyone

muninga
niové
obeche
olive
opepe
ovangkol
padauk, African
poga
rapanea
sapele
satinwood
'teak, Rhodesian'
utile
walnut, African

GUN STOCKS

mahogany, African ; niové ; walnut, African.

INSULATION

ceiba ; erimado.

JOINERY

High class

abura
afara
afrormosia
afzelia
agba
aningeria
camphorwood
celtis, African
ekaba
ekebergia
ekop
ekoune
gedu nohor
guarea
idigbo
iroko
kanda

longui rouge
mafu
mahogany, African
makoré
malacantha
mansonia
mtambara
mugonyone
muninga
niové
omu
ovangkol
poga
sapele
utile
walnut, African
cypress

Utility

adjouaba
akossika
albizia
alstonia
antiaris
ayan
canarium, African
ceiba
cordia
difou
gheombi
ilomba
izombe
musizi

niangon
obeche
ogea
ollem
ozigo
limbali
pencil cedar
pillarwood
podo
pterygota
radiata pine
safoukala
sterculia, brown

LABORATORY FITTINGS

abura; afrormosia; afzelia; iroko; makoré.

MARINE PILING AND CONSTRUCTION

Under water

(a) Teredo infested waters

afrormosia
afzelia
albizia (heavy)
ekki
esia
idigbo
iroko

makoré
muhuhu
mukulungu
muninga
'oak, African'
okan
opepe

(b) Non teredo waters
In addition to the above,
agba; dahoma; guarea; utile.

Above water
(a) Docks, wharves, bridges, etc.

afzelia
ekki
iroko
makarati

missanda
muhimbi
'oak, African'
opepe

(b) Decking

afrormosia
iroko
malacantha
mueri

muhuhu
mukulungu
okan
opepe

MUSICAL INSTRUMENTS

blackwood
boxwood
cordia
ebony, African

mahogany, African
mansonia
sapele
utile

PATTERNMAKING

abura; mahogany, African; izombe

SHOP FITTINGS

abura
afara
afzelia
agba
avodiré
danta
gedu nohor
grevillea
idigbo

iroko
mansonia
niangon
opepe
padauk, African
poga
sapele
utile
walnut, African

SILLS AND THRESHOLDS

afrormosia
afzelia
agba

dahoma
makoré
opepe

SPORTS GOODS

agba
berlinia
celtis, African
danta
ebony, African
ekki
gaboon
guarea

longui rouge
mahogany, African
obeche
padauk, African
podo
sapele
utile

STAIR TREADS

afrormosia
afzelia
ekki

iroko
opepe

TOOL HANDLES

blackwood (knife)
celtis, African
danta

makarati
olive
padauk, African (knife)

TOPS FOR COUNTERS

afrormosia
afzelia
guarea
iroko

mahogany, African
sapele
utile

TURNERY

abura
blackwood
boxwood
bubinga
danta
difou
ebony, African
ekaba
ekoune
guarea
iroko
izombe

limbali
longui rouge
mahogany, African
makoré
mansonia
mugonyone
mukulungu
odoko
olive
opepe
ovangkol
padauk, African

VEHICLE—BODY WORK

abura
agba
albizia
ayan
berlinia
dahoma
danta
iroko

limbali
longui rouge
makarati
makoré
malacantha
mueri
mugonyone
opepe

VENEER AND PLYWOOD

Corestock

akossika
antiaris
canarium, African
ceiba
gmelina
igaganga

ilomba
kondrotti
obeche
ogea
ollem
pterygota

Decorative

afara
afzelia
aningeria
avodiré *
bubinga
difou
ebony, African
ekaba
ekoune
gheombi
grevillea
guarea
iroko
izombe

lingui rouge
mahogany, African
makoré
moabi
niové
omu
ovangkol
sapele
tetraberlinia
thuya burr
utile
walnut, African
wenge

Utility †

abura
adjouaba
afara
agba
akossika
aningeria
avodiré
difou
ekoune
gaboon
gheombi

idigbo
igaganga
mafu
mtambara
okwen
ozigo
podo
pterygota
safoukala
sterculia, brown

* ex selected figured logs

† utility veneer for plywood manufacture, with or without decorative face veneer, chip baskets, and small laminated articles.

AMENABILITY OF HEARTWOOD TO PRESERVATIVE TREATMENT

Extremely resistant

afrormosia
afzelia
albizia
avodiré
banga wanga
blackwood
camphorwood
canarium, African
difou
ebony, African
ekki
esia
gedu nohor
guarea
iroko
kanda
limbali
mahogany, African
makoré
mansonia
moabi
muhimbi
niangon
okan
okwen
sterculia, brown
sterculia, yellow
'teak, Rhodesian'
utile
'walnut, African'

Resistant

adjouaba
agba
ayan
berlinia
cordia
dahoma
danta
ekaba
gheombi
igaganga
izombe
muninga
obeche
omu
ozigo
sapele

Moderately resistant

abura
afara
celtis, African
ekoune
gmelina
longui rouge
mtambara
ogea
opepe
safoukala

Permeable

akossika
alstonia
aningeria
antiaris
bombax
ceiba
ilomba
musizi
odoko
pterygota

AMENABILITY OF HEARTWOOD TO PRESERVATIVE TREATMENT

The above classification refers to the ease with which a timber absorbs preservatives under both open-tank (non-pressure) and pressure treatments. Sapwood, although nearly always perishable, is usually much more permeable than heartwood, accordingly, the above classification refers to the relative resistance of heartwood to penetration.

Extremely resistant
Timbers that absorb only a small amount of preservative even under long pressure treatments. They cannot be penetrated to an appreciable depth laterally, and only to a very small extent longitudinally.

Resistant
Timbers difficult to impregnate under pressure and require a long period of treatment. It is often difficult to penetrate them laterally more than about 3mm to 6mm.
Incising is often used to obtain better treatment.

Moderately resistant
Timbers that are fairly easy to treat, and it is usually possible to obtain a lateral penetration of the order of 6mm to 18mm in about 2-3 hours under pressure, or a penetration of a large proportion of the vessels.

Permeable
Timbers that can be penetrated completely under pressure without difficulty, and can usually be heavily impregnated by the open-tank process.

RESISTANCE TO MARINE BORERS*

Very durable

afrormosia
afzelia
albizia
ekki
esia
iroko
makoré
missanda

muhuhu
mukulungu
muninga
oak, African
okan
opepe
padauk, African
teak, Rhodesian

Moderately durable

agba
ayan
banga wanga
berlinia
dahoma
danta

guarea
idigbo
malacantha
mansonia
utile
walnut, African

Non-durable

abura
afara
alstonia
antiaris
bombax
camphorwood
canarium, African
ceiba
celtis, African
cordia
gaboon
gedu nohor
ilomba

loliondo
mahogany, African
mugonha
muhimbi
musizi
obeche
odoko
ogea
okwen
omu
pillarwood
pterygota
sapele

*Marine borers: This classification is based mainly upon TRADA exposure trials at Shoreham; durability should be interpreted as follows:—

Very durable	Suitable under conditions of heavy attack by *Teredo* and *Limnoria*.
Moderately durable	Suitable under conditions of moderate attack, mainly *Limnoria*.

| Non-durable | unsuitable, or suitable only for short service life. |

For further information see TRADA publication, 'Timber for marine and fresh water construction'.

TERMITE RESISTANCE (HEARTWOOD) *

Termites, (order Isoptera). The classification is based upon the reputed resistance to attack by both dry-wood and subterranean termites. Where the resistance to either type differs, the lower rating is given.

Very resistant
makoré, muhuhu.

Resistant

afzelia
agba
albizia
E. A. camphorwood
danta
ekki
esia
iroko
izombe
kanda
missanda
muhimbi

mukulungu
muninga
okan
okwen *(B. leonensis)*
olive
opepe
padauk, African
panga-panga
sterculia-brown
'teak, Rhodesian'
wenge

Moderately resistant

ayan
berlinia
dahoma
ebony, African
ekaba
gaboon
gedu nohor
gmelina

guarea
idigbo
limbali
longui rouge
mansonia
omu
sapele
'walnut, African'

132

Non-resistant

abura
afara
akossika
alstonia
aningeria
antiaris
bombax
canarium, African
ceiba
celtis, African
cordia
Dacryodes spp.
difou
ekoune

gheombi
ilomba
makarati
musizi
obeche
odoko
ogea
okwen *(B. eurycoma)*
pillarwood
pterygota
rapanea
sterculia, yellow
utile

REFERENCES

BOLZA, Eleanor and KEATING, W G. African timbers—the properties, uses and characteristics of 700 species. Melbourne, Australia, Division of Building Research. 1972.

BRITISH STANDARDS INSTITUTION. Nomenclature of commercial timbers, including sources of supply. British Standard 881 & 589. London, BSI. 1974.

BUILDING RESEARCH ESTABLISHMENT. A handbook of softwoods. Building Research Establishment Report. 2nd edition. London, HMSO. 1977.

KRYN, Jeannette M and FOBES, E W. Woods of Liberia. US. Forest Products Laboratory Report 2159. Madison, FPL. 1959.

OKIGBO, L. Some Nigerian woods. 2nd edition. Lagos, Federal Ministry of Information. 1964.

PRINCES RISBOROUGH LABORATORY. Handbook of hardwoods, revised by R H Farmer. 2nd edition. London, HMSO. 1972.

The TRADA series of red booklets—'Timbers of the World'

1 Timbers of Africa

2 Timbers of South America

3 Timbers of Southern Asia

4 Timbers of South East Asia

5 Timbers of Philippines and Japan

6 Timbers of Europe

7 Timbers of North America

8 Timbers of Australasia

9 Timbers of Central America and Caribbean

INDEX

138

P

142

Scotland
TRADA, Beresford House,
5/6 Claremont Terrace
GLASGOW G3 7XR
041 332 4491

North east
TRADA, 11 Bank Street
WETHERBY
West Yorkshire LS22 4NQ
0937 61543

Midlands
TRADA, Cavalier House
202 Hagley Road
EDGBASTON B16 9PP
021 454 8292

TRADA Officer - Republic of Ireland
10 Orwell Road
Rathgar
DUBLIN 6
Dublin 962666